HOF

THIS BOOK CONTAINS:

Marie's Diary - extracts from Marie Campion's Diary,
which she kept since she was eleven years old

Personally Speaking - writings by sufferers from eating disorders

Action Days - suggestions to aid recovery

MARIE CAMPION

Marie Campion is an Eating Distress Counsellor
working in the clinic she set up with her husband in
Marino, Dublin. She herself suffered from an eating
disorder for over twenty years, and her experiences are
revealed in the Diary sections of this book. She then
studied therapy and is a member of the Academy for
Eating Disorders.

Her therapy centre is:
The Marino Therapy Centre,
22 Marino Mart, Fairview, Dublin 3.
Helpline: (01) 2600 366.

Hope

Marie Campion

ILLUSTRATIONS
Emma Walsh

THE O'BRIEN PRESS
DUBLIN

First published 1998 by The O'Brien Press Ltd.,
20 Victoria Road, Rathgar, Dublin 6, Ireland.
Tel. +353 1 4923333 Fax. +353 1 4922777
e-mail: books@obrien.ie
http://www.obrien.ie

ISBN: 0-86278-562-6

British Library Cataloguing-in-publication Data
Campion, Marie
Hope : understanding eating disorders
1.Eating Disorders - Popular works
I.Title
616.8'526

1 2 3 4 5 6 7 8 9 10
98 99 00 01 02 03 04 05 06

Typesetting, layout, design: The O'Brien Press Ltd.
Cover design: designit
Cover separations: Lithoset Ltd.
Printing: The Guernsey Press Ltd.

NOTE In order to protect identities names in this book have been changed.

CONTENTS

INTRODUCTION

This is a book on eating disorders. Our purpose is not to tell sufferers how to recover, but to remind them that they can do it because other people did. We do not present case studies or a deep analysis of what causes eating disorders. Here we share the real stories of people who have overcome or are overcoming their difficulties in relation to food. We do this with the intention of encouraging sufferers, to remind them that they are not alone in this frightening illness and that there is light for them at the end of the tunnel.

People who have an eating disorder usually suffer from either anorexia nervosa, bulimia nervosa or compulsive eating. Until recently very little was known about this 'secret' illness. Anorexia nervosa was first documented in 1964 by a London physician who reported the condition in a 16-year-old male. Even though it is a widespread illness it was not properly described until 1968 when the complexity of emotional, physical and psychological aspects associated with the illness were uncovered.

Anorexia sufferers usually share the following characteristics:

- ~ fear of gaining weight
- ~ distorted body image
- ~ missing monthly menstruation
- ~ withdrawal from all social contacts
- ~ perfectionist compulsions
- ~ a feeling of cold
- ~ dizziness and fainting spells
- ~ a tendency to dress in layers in order to hide oneself
- ~ fear of situations where food may be present

~ a rigid exercise programme

~ insecurities about personal capabilities.

The main characteristics of bulimia are as follows:

~ repeated episodes of binge eating with or without self-induced vomiting

~ laxative and diuretics abuse

~ diet pills abuse

~ over exercising

~ complaints of fatigue and muscle pain

~ swollen glands

~ puffiness in the cheeks, broken blood vessels under eyes

~ tooth decay

~ weight fluctuation, often within a 10 to 20 pound range

~ preoccupation with and constant talk about food and weight

~ mood shifts and depression, sadness, severe guilt and self-hate

~ self-worth determined by weight.

Compusive eating involves:

~ constantly eating through the day, or occasional binges

~ eating in secret, often at night

~ a feeling of being out of control around food

~ a pattern of strict dieting, possible abuse of laxatives, diuretics and slimming tablets

~ hypertension or fatigue

~ an inability to maintain constant weight

~ mood swings

~ guilt and shame about amount eaten

~ loss of interest in sexual activity

~ possible malnutrition, because of poor diet

Compulsive eating is only beginning to be recognised as an illness; it is still not included in the official list of psychiatric conditions. It is definitely a psychological disorder in which food is used unknowingly to cope with stress, emotional conflict and daily problems. Dieting is mistakenly seen as the solution and is undertaken with strenuous effort; feelings of deprivation set in because dieting is usually approached in a rigid manner.

People are driven to compulsive eating through suppressed anger, loneliness, stress in work. Very often they have a tendency to pretend the problem does not exist. They try to cope with it alone because there is so little recognition of this form of eating disorder.

Our society is desperately trying to become thinner. It seems that the average healthy body is not enough anymore. The body is no longer viewed as a gift of nature, but as an object which we can sculpt to our liking, which we must manufacture for other people's approval. The body has become an expression of the way we feel. Our culture has become very superficial; we are living extremely stressed, pressurised lives; we are distancing ourselves further from nature; we are developing even more internal stress; we feel pressurised to put our energy into external impressions and we forget that it is our relationships which count; we have fallen victim to consumerism and to the seduction of advertisements. All of this has become fertile ground for the development of eating disorders.

Research reveals that contrary to popular myths about eating disorders, the illness does not discriminate; it is found among males and females, across all socio-economic classes, in many races, and in all age groups.

In the USA more that 8 million people are suffering from an eating disorder and in Great Britain an estimated 600,000 people are in treatment. Research has also shown that 80 per cent of Americans have dieted by the age of 18, and in Great Britain one out of four is on a diet. Alarming research from Swansea University has shown that 25 per cent of children under seven years of age want to diet even though they are the correct body weight. In Ireland, a study undertaken by the Dublin Institute of Technology in collaboration with Trinity College and the Eastern Health Board has shown that seven out of every ten of the 420 young girls interviewed are trying to lose weight even though almost a third of them perceive themselves as being normal weight or even underweight.

Those who suffer from an eating disorder carry around with them a terrible secret. For over twenty years I carried the sufferer's secret. I lived in fear that people would find out the real me – the bad one, the one who had nothing to offer to this world, to anybody.

From early childhood I felt different. I could not understand this feeling, but I was ashamed of it. I wanted to have somebody to trust, to share how I felt, but I was afraid that if anybody discovered the real me they would be terrified and never want to see me again.

From about the age of nine I developed an eating problem: gradually it became more and more difficult to eat. Suddenly people were noticing me, worrying about me, fussing over me. I was important. For several years home became a battle ground but I solved this problem by eating and then getting rid of the food through vomiting. I had developed bulimia, a condition which at that time did not even have a name. I had become a good girl again, not a difficult one. And this became my big secret for nearly twenty years. It was my very own secret. When I reflect on all the negative feelings connected with this secret I feel sad, but no longer for myself. I survived and let them go. My sadness is for the thousands of people who are now going through this confusing condition.

I have felt a great desire to help other sufferers. When I was at my worst, when my life consisted only of binges or severe starvation, when I was told by experts that I would never recover, that I would have to live with it and control it, I read an article in a women's magazine about another person who went through similar experiences. She wrote about how wonderful it felt to have recovered and be free of this obsession. That was one of my breaking points. If she did it, I could do it too.

It took many years of hardship, of ups and downs, before I was able to call myself 'fully recovered'. There were a lot of moments and even days and weeks when I doubted my ability to do it. 'Maybe she is much stronger than I am, maybe others can recover and I cannot, maybe it is too late for me ...' These were the thoughts that held me back, but in the end I did it; it never came back and the result was well worth it.

Today, on the other side of the condition, I can see the world differently. My life was not the problem, my body was not the problem, people around me were not the problem. The problem was my attitude to all that was happening. At the time I did not know any other way. I had to revise my thinking about myself, about my values, about life itself.

After working with hundreds of people in the process of recovery I have become more and more convinced that to enable people to recover we all need to increase our understanding of what eating disorders are and their function in people's lives. Eating disorders are not about food only. This is actually the smallest part of the illness, the most obvious manifestation of the self-destructive thinking of the person. Eating disorders are the expression of an inability to accept oneself, a crisis of identity. For sufferers, the person they are is just never good enough, never perfect enough. The condition is literally self-denial in an extreme form.

What is recovery, what is cure? Usually people who have never suffered from this illness, especially parents, partners and some of the medical professionals, tend to look for a short-term answer, concentrating on the food issue. Working on the food issue only is like building a house with no foundation. The first strong wind will knock this house down. Eating disorders develop slowly, and so recovery also comes slowly. In recovery, there are no quick fixes, there are no short cuts. Recovery is a process and it takes a long time. If we want to help a person in recovery we have to give them this time and help them tackle the underlying difficulty in accepting themselves. Putting pressure on the person is never a help; it can be a barrier. From my own experience the less we pressurise, the better the chances of recovery. We need to listen to sufferers, listen to their needs, not tell them what to do or try to do it for them.

Eating disorders do not start when a person begins to lose or put on weight or take a laxative, vomit, or over-exercise. These are only the symptoms of the condition, the signs of a much deeper problem. Eating disorders are about people's feelings and emotions, the way people perceive themselves and the way they think others view them. When you go through this illness you spend so much mental energy on wanting to be liked by others that there is no energy left for coping with life. And even if you are loved and liked you do not allow yourself to believe it. It is a vicious circle. It becomes easier to feel negative about yourself than to accept yourself the way you are. Negativity becomes a protection against hurt, against reality and against disappointments. It is the only security you allow yourself to have. Sometimes negativity is the only thing you know at that time and self-destructive behaviour becomes a ventilation of this way of thinking; this in turn reinforces the negative state of mind.

If we want to help a person to recover from an eating disorder, we must not concentrate on the physical symptoms only. We must not try to take their patterns of behaviour from people without showing them some other choices. Often this is the only feeling of control they have. We need to see the person and her or his quality as a human being first and then we can work with the behaviour.

Forcing an underweight person to eat or an overweight person to lose weight is only a short-term solution which usually does not last and in some cases can be even dangerous. Who are we helping here? Are we helping ourselves or them? Should we feel better if our daughters or sons put on weight or lose weight, or should we first care if they are mentally ready to do it? Research shows that fluctuating weight can do more damage to our bodies than being underweight or overweight. Having rosy cheeks is not recovery; this is not psychological health. Recovery means taking responsibility for our health, which includes healthy weight, and feeling good about it.

Recovery from an eating disorder is a long-term process. We need to learn to take one step at a time and not to expect miracles. We need to concentrate on weight restoration or health restoration more than on weight gain or weight loss. Strict behavioural treatment leads to the minimising of important issues in psychological functioning; it can cause relapses. Treatment for recovery needs to be orientated towards learning to think differently about body weight and shape, to find the human goals behind this condition. Factors included in recovery should involve not only diagnoses but also awareness of personality structure, the person's age, family history and family structure.

A belief that one can master life's problems and develop attainable goals will always be essential to reclaiming one's freedom. Recovery means developing healthy coping skills in order to reach a sense of responsibility for actions, behaviour and feelings, and achieving the ability to experience all the joys of life without fear or worry.

Recovery is possible. It was possible for me. Today I do not see my years of eating disorder as wasted. They were years of education for me. I learned all about life and realised that there is so much to live for. I have dedicated the rest of my life to helping others find their true qualities and live healthy, happy lives. I hope this book will encourage you to believe that everybody on this earth has something to offer, and so do you!

Marie Campion
July 1998

Winning starts with beginning.

DO YOU ...? OR DO YOU KNOW SOMEONE WHO DOES?

Read this carefully and decide if this book is for you.

- ~ Do you constantly think about food?
- ~ Do you starve occasionally?
- ~ Are you constantly going on diets?
- ~ Are you bingeing?
- ~ Do you always feel too full after a meal?
- ~ Do you feel guilty about what you have eaten?
- ~ Do you count every calorie you eat?
- ~ Is your size affecting the way you live your life?
- ~ Does your behaviour with food make you and other people around you feel unhappy?
- ~ Do you eat or not eat when you are stressed?
- ~ Do you put off decisions until you 'lose weight'?
- ~ Do you frequently compare your looks to others?
- ~ Does your perception of how you look depend on the amount you eat?
- ~ Do you exercise to lose weight rather than for enjoyment?
- ~ Do you feel isolated?
- ~ Do you begin a diet every morning?
- ~ Are you taking diet pills?
- ~ Do you hide food?
- ~ Do you feel groggy after eating?
- ~ Do you eat when you are bored?
- ~ Do you feel depressed about the way you eat?
- ~ Is how you look very important to you?
- ~ Do you exercise to excess?
- ~ Do you change the way you eat all the time?

~ Do you feel ashamed of your body size?

~ Do you have guilt feelings related to your eating behaviour?

~ Do your eating habits cost you an excessive amount of money?

~ Do you take laxatives?

~ Do you weigh yourself daily?

~ Do you avoid discussion of your food problem?

~ Do you throw up food?

You may be suffering from some of these symptoms. If you are, here are some tips to help you deal with them:

◊ Put yourself first. You can't be anything for anybody else unless you take care of yourself.

◊ When you need something, don't talk yourself out of it. Even if you can't have it, it's okay to need it.

◊ When you are angry, let yourself feel the anger. Decide what you want to do about it; express it or take some action in relation to it.

◊ When you are sad, think about what would be comforting.

◊ When you are hurt, talk to the person who hurt you; keeping it inside makes it grow.

◊ When you want something from someone else, ask. You'll be okay if they say no. Asking is being true to yourself.

◊ When you feel alone, know there are people who want to be with you. Fantasise what it would be like to be with each of them. Decide if you want to make that happen.

◊ If you are doing something like overeating or starving, stop. Think about what you really want. If you are stuck and cannot think clearly, talk out loud to someone.

◊ When you can't think clearly, stop thinking – feel!

To the question of life, you are the only answer.
To the problems of your life, you are the only solution.

1

RECOVERY IS FOR YOU

Every day we create the life we live. And life, even for food sufferers, is for living, loving and learning. The more we learn about the body, how it works and what is essential for good health, the easier it becomes to create the life we want. We only have one body and it must last a lifetime, so we should learn to be its protector and friend. Proper care for our body is reflected in a healthy mind and a happy outlook on life.

Fashion...

50's 60's 70's 80's 90's WHAT NEXT?

Through the years.....

When we suffer from an eating disorder we experience many negative emotions, and these can have a very destructive influence on us. We need to learn to heal ourselves. This takes much time and effort. But it is possible; the human mind and the human body have enormous self-healing capacities.

To recover, we need to appreciate the fact that we have all the resources within ourselves to get better. We need to understand that everything we ever do has an effect on our body, our mind, our spirituality. We need to accept that the whole person must be taken into account, not only the physical symptoms of the illness. We need to realise that having an eating disorder is not our fault, but we have a choice to do something about it.

Recovery involves looking closely at our lifestyle, our emotional, nutritional and physical states, all of which interact and contribute to the overall situation. It involves making a decision that it is never too late to start a new life.

Those of us who suffer from an eating disorder tend to look at past years as 'wasted'; we feel regret that we have lost so much time. But in fact that time is not wasted. It is important learning material. Understanding it will help us change the picture. What is crucial is that we first become really sick of the sickness, move ahead bravely, come to terms with the past and grasp the future.

PATIENCE

One of the most important steps in recovery is to recognise that an eating disorder is a problem that cannot be solved through sheer willpower. We must learn to be patient with ourselves, because recovery does take time and requires a lot of mental and physical energy. It is not always a smooth journey. The path can go up and down. Every setback should be taken as a learning experience which will lead us to further understanding.

Essentially we are learning to control our life rather than our body. Gradually we exchange 'eating or starving' for coping and living. Under the obsession of overeating and starving we lose our control of life. It is our responsibility to look for it again. Sometimes we need outside help, for example a doctor, a therapist, a book, but the truth is that it is only we who can do it. We can use their guidance, their support, but only we can do the work.

SELF-KNOWLEDGE

If we allow ourselves to see ourselves in a negative way we end up depressed and hopeless. Most people have low self-esteem because they do not know themselves. We need to learn about all the pluses and minuses of our personality.

The more positive information we gather about ourselves, the easier it will be to make positive decisions. We need to know what our food problem is giving us and learn to give ourselves more positive choices.

Self-knowledge is a journey of discovering our own self-worth and how to manage ourselves. It can be scary to explore the unknown. Yet keeping parts of ourselves hidden drains our energy and creativity and is a loss of potential.

SELF-AWARENESS

Why do we need to be aware of ourselves? It is because it enables us to visualise where and who we are, and mentally rehearse possible actions for the future. Letting go of a food problem starts with taking charge of our life, and taking charge begins with awareness. We learn to be aware of ourselves in the present and to take life minute by minute.

Self-awareness is one of our strongest tools in conquering an eating disorder. It sheds a bright light on the darkness of our negative thinking. With awareness comes choice: we begin to see possibilities for a positive future and to wake up to the reality of our individuality.

Awareness is not judgement. It is the quality of attention which observes what we are doing without pushing us in a particular direction. It is a voice that notices everything around us. As soon as we are aware of our behaviour, we can give ourselves another choice.

Self-awareness operates at many levels. Body-awareness is a crucial element in relation to eating disorders. We need to be aware of the difference between wanting and needing. Recovery is learning to live in the world, with food, not for it. It is important to be aware of the rewards that we get from our relationships with food, rewards that keep the relationship going. Awareness is important for finding alternative rewards.

When we suffer from an eating disorder we are usually very dissatisfied with our body and we do not even want to be aware of it. Often we even hate ourselves and punish it in the extreme. We have an ideal weight in mind, but the minute we reach it there is always the 'extra pound' to shed. We feel that this will make the big difference to our lives.

Awareness of feelings is also very important. Often our feelings are so suppressed that we are almost unaware that we have them. We must acknowledge our feelings, and only then can we let them go.

Food problems are not about food; they are about feelings. Negative feelings are within ourselves; they are not the reality around us. The reality around us changes when we change these negative feelings. Unfortunately we often try to change the reality instead of the feelings.

Awareness allows us to see how much we mean to others. It allows us to accept ourselves as good people. It helps us realise that we are better than we ever believed. Awareness is about self-observation, watching ourselves; that is totally different to self-absorption or self-preoccupation. Self-observation is carefully watching what is happening to us and others and trying to learn from it. The reason we suffer from depression and anxieties is that instead of dissociating from negative feelings, we identify with them. Often we put all our effort into 'fixing things' instead of observing them, being aware of them, understanding them. Food problems need to be understood, not fixed. Later, change can take place.

SELF-ACCEPTANCE

The term self-acceptance can sometimes cause panic to those of us who suffer from an eating disorder. We connect self-acceptance with a life of misery, but in reality it is the first step towards making a real and lasting change.

Self-acceptance does not close the door on change. On the contrary, it can open up our inner resources so that we can explore ourselves in a more relaxed way. It develops the capacity for good personal relations. People with a high level of self-acceptance are likely to be less defensive and it is easier for them to tolerate others. Through acceptance we learn to treat ourselves the way we've always wished others would. We do not need to wait for others to accept us as we are. We can start living with ourselves in a new way, and this allows us to move ahead.

Acceptance means that we acknowledge what our body looks like without berating ourselves. This acceptance is not stagnation; it is the next step to changing and living. We spend a lot of time and energy rejecting, hating, denying parts or all of who we are. We should put all that time and energy into accepting ourselves.

Acceptance does not mean giving up. It means that we appreciate the fact that recovery takes time; it means coming to terms with the fact that there are some things which we cannot change. People who accept themselves are not over-critical of themselves or others; they are both compassionate and realistic. They look at themselves as they are and strive for a better understanding of what they want to change. We cannot remove a problem until we accept we have one. Acceptance helps us to move on instead of postponing and wanting the impossible. In recovery some days can be better than others. In the process we learn to accept ourselves for what we are. When we suffer from an eating disorder we live a life of 'if only ... '. Most of the times the 'if only ...' is a wish for magical change, but it prevents a realistic approach to change. The 'if only' syndrome automatically puts us down. Learning to accept ourselves and the reality in which we find ourselves helps us to move onwards.

SELF-ESTEEM

People with an eating disorder usually have very low self-esteem. The only cure for this condition is a massive dose of self-love. In our society we are brought up to believe that loving ourselves is selfish and wrong. Gradually we realise that not loving and not believing in ourselves is even worse. We are actually born with a sense of self-love and importance. Most children see themselves as beautiful and very important. As we grow up our sense of self-worth is gradually knocked down. Messages of self-doubt are reinforced on us from all around: Do we look good? What do others think of us?

If we feel bad and unworthy, food is very often the plaster and the cure for those feelings. By learning to feel important, worthy and beautiful again we recognise how good we are, and realise that everybody is unique. It is the little imperfection that makes people attractive and interesting. People with an eating disorder are often thinking more about others than themselves, and trying to give of themselves as much as they can. But how can you give yourself if you feel worthless?

If we love ourselves we have no need for gimmicks; we are not doing something for notice, attention or thanks, but from the genuine pleasure of giving. As sufferers of an eating disorder we can spend too much time and effort trying to win the approval of others. Often other people's approval is needed for us to be satisfied with ourselves. Approval of others should be only a bonus in our lives, not a necessity. Approval-seeking is connected with misery and frustration in our lives. If we do not have strong self-esteem our sense of self is sacrificed to the opinions and predictions of others; we absorb a negative message: 'Do not trust yourself.'

Our self-belief is the cornerstone of self-esteem and makes recovery permanent. If we believe we are worthless and incapable, then the impression we project to others will be a reflection of these internalised opinions. People act through their beliefs; these beliefs are learned and they can be unlearned or relearned. Preconditioning can have a very strong effect on our beliefs. If we tell ourselves how awful, incapable or unlucky we are – we believe it. When we change how we think about ourselves, the world around us also changes. When we change our beliefs, we change our life. It is our self-belief which helps us to overcome our problem with eating. The journey is very hard and very long and we can get there only if we believe that we can do it.

'Happiness is not something you experience,
it is something you remember.' Oscar Levant

2

WHEN CAN IT START?

Anybody can suffer from an eating disorder. Eating disorders don't discriminate, they aren't confined to a particular group of people, they can affect children, teenagers, women and men of all ages. The eating disorder develops on a subconscious level before any physical symptoms appear, such as bingeing, starving, over-exercising and laxative abuse.

The development of this condition can be prevented and that can be done only with high awareness and a deep understanding. In this chapter, through entries from Marie's diary, we point out a few symptoms which can lead to the development of this illness.

Parents should watch out for such symptoms. It is important to be aware that complex negative feelings can appear at a very early age.

Sunday, 15 May 1966

Dear friend,

I am so unhappy today, I need to talk to someone. But who? I'm sure they would laugh at me if I told them what is happening to me. It is becoming a problem. I think it's a problem. You see, nobody understands me. I'm sure everybody would think I'm crazy. So that is why I have decided to write to you.

Please be my friend. I really do need someone to talk to. Okay, so you are just this piece of paper, or are you someone I can see in my mind, my imaginary friend? I need a friend. I just know that it is important for me to have someone. I need someone. I need you. Please be my friend. You are special. You will listen to me. I know you will understand. You see I am very, very lonely.

Oh, I'm sorry, you don't even know who I am. Let me introduce myself. My name is Marie. It was my birthday yesterday. I was eleven. Yes, eleven already. Everybody was remarking and saying ... Oh Marie, you are such a big girl ... I hate it when they say that. I know I am a big girl. I do not have to be reminded of the fact. Big Girl - I just cannot stand those words. I know I am bigger than any of my friends at school and much fatter as well.

This morning I was looking at myself in the mirror. I was disgusted with what I saw. I am so ugly. My face is round and looks like the moon. My legs are as big as a Japanese wrestler, and I feel so awkward. How could anybody like a girl like me?

I do not know what to do about myself. Maybe I should try to eat less, but how could I explain that to my mother? Every time we have our dinner, there is a full plate of food put in front of me and the usual comments with it. 'Come on, Marie, it's good for you. You need your food. It's full of vitamins. You're a growing girl. Let me see the plate empty now ...'

I know I'm growing. It's repeated to me so often, how could I ever forget it, even if I wanted to! Don't they realise I do not want to be any bigger! Surely they must realise that. It is easy for Mother to talk, she is so beautiful and slim, and my father loves her. I'm so ugly, nobody could ever love me.

Some time ago I was reading a magazine that belonged to my mother. In it were several diets, and it showed you how to lose pounds in just weeks. I was thrilled. This could be the answer to my prayers. But how would I get away with it and not be noticed? How would I explain to mother? She would lose the head, freak out, and then it would end up with her not talking to me for days. Worse still, she would get upset and think I did not like her cooking, which she is so proud of. She cooks and bakes often, and expects me to eat everything she prepares. It's very hard to say 'No' to Mother.

It's not only the food that is a problem. It's also the way I have to dress. She buys lovely clothes, really expensive dresses. But she still dresses me like a four-year-old baby. She never asks my opinion on anything. It's still frills and bows with everything. Ugh, I'm still her baby. She never lets go. I would love to wear my type of clothes - you know, what the others wear. I would certainly be more comfortable. It would be much more me.

So as you can see I have a good bit on my mind. I do need someone. Thank you.

Marie

Sunday, 5 June 1966

Dear friend,

It's good to talk to you. No, honestly, it is great to have someone to talk to. Thanks for being here for me. I'm feeling much better today. I have some good news for you today. Well, I think it is good news. I hope you will agree. Unfortunately I still look the same, ugly and fat. But the good news is that I am going to do something about my appearance. I'm going to change my image.

First, I have stopped eating sweets. That was not too hard. There are never too many sweets around the house anyway. But I feel like I am doing something positive. I have not lost any weight, but I have not gained any either. That is great.

About ten days ago I was watching a fashion show on television. I was fascinated with the whole show, but in particular with the beautiful girls. I just could not take my eyes off them. They were so lovely. Not that I want to become a model or anything like that. Oh no, that is not my dream. I want to be a doctor. But I certainly would like to look like those models and have their shape. I am determined that I will look like them one day.

I have worked out a plan. I cut out pictures of the beautiful slim girls from Mother's fashion magazines. I put them in my drawer and I look at them before my meals to remind myself that this is how I will look if I keep to my plan.

Another thing I have done is, with my pocket money I bought a book called HOW TO LOSE POUNDS AND FEEL BETTER. It's fantastic. Everything I want to know about calories and how many calories I need to take per day. The book contains lots of low-calorie recipes, different exercises for each morning and evening. It will be hard going because I hate physical exercise. In school I am always making excuses to avoid it. I feel clumsy and so awkward and big. I feel ashamed. I am much slower than the other girls. We have to wear shorts and I'm sure I look like a boxer.

But things are going to be different. I can feel it. Because with the help of this book I will be happy. There are special exercises for losing inches on different parts of your body. One exercise shows how to make your hips thinner. Another one for your stomach - that one I need the most. I hate wearing skirts, because my stomach sticks out and I look pregnant. But I will work hard on this area.

There are pictures of women who have lost twenty to forty pounds or more. You should see the difference it can make. They look much better and they admit they feel better in themselves and as a result they have become much happier. I will be happier. I know I would be better looking if I could only lose some weight.

The biggest problem is, how I am going to tell my parents that I have decided to try this diet? I can see already how Mother will react. She will lose her temper. She will be angry and shout as if everybody around has gone suddenly deaf. This always happens when she does not get her way. After a while she'll calm down and be sorry. It's always the same. Now if Father is at home, he usually calms her down quickly. He is so peaceful and hates arguments of any kind. He always says, 'things can be solved quietly without the storm.' It is a pity Mother forgets so conveniently.

One thing I am sure about is, this plan is not going to be easy. But I am going to stay on this diet, hassle or not. Maybe I should not tell them anything, keep it between you and me, that maybe is the best. Both my parents are out all day working. Breakfast and lunch will be easy. My biggest problem will be the evening meal but as I said I am so determined to stick to my plan, no matter what the cost, no matter how much hassle it brings. I will see it through. The decision is made. I am going to lose weight, and I am going to be happy.

Marie

3

TRAPPED IN A BIG BUBBLE

When people go through an eating disorder they feel like they are trapped, trapped in a big bubble. The world around them seems strange and alien. They feel scared, not understood. They often do not understand themselves. In order to help them or be there for them we need to learn how they feel; we need to learn to understand what actually goes on in their mind.

In this chapter we are trying to convey how it really feels when you cannot reach out or be reached by others even if you would love to, when you cannot concentrate on your work or homework and you really have to, when you cannot eat and you really have to ... when you cannot cope anymore and you really have to.

TRAPPED IN A BIG BUBBLE

Emma

Sometimes when I'm walking somewhere in school I feel like I'm trapped in a big bubble. I don't really know exactly what that means but it's a good description of how I feel. It's really scary. I'm totally alone and I feel so different to everyone else. Really weird and strange. And when I'm sitting on the steps or somewhere and people walk past me, they're pitying me – the poor loner, no friends, sitting on the cold steps on her own because she's too scared to enter the lunch room, too intimidated. It's all written plainly on their faces. It's so obvious.

It's like, sometimes I begin to feel again the same way I felt when I was abroad for the first time. The same scary, lonely, out-of-my-depth feeling. The trapped feeling, no security, having no one I know, no one I trust, no one even to talk to. It's so terrifying. I hate it. I hope things get better, but sometimes I really believe there's no way out. It's like a dead end. Nothing left, nothing after that.

DON'T ASK ME WHY

Maria

Why does she worry, why does she cry?
Why is there always a tear in her eye?
Why is she lonely, why is she blue?
Why does she long to be just like you?
Why does she fear, why does she hide?
Why does she feel so empty inside?
Why is there now just a bottomless pit?
Where once, long ago, her heart did sit?
Why do they tease her,
You're ugly, you're fat, and that's how you'll stay?

Why does the hurt cut so deep like a knife?
Maybe it's time to give up on life.
Why you may ask, why you may say,
Why won't her hunger and pain go away?
Why is the question; the answer you'll find,
When you stop asking why and open your mind.

HUNGER

Emma

Sitting upstairs, trying to concentrate on her homework, her head is pounding. The words are blurred on the page and her hand is shaking. Her stomach is empty.

She feels light-headed, giddy, dizzy; her hands won't stop shaking and her stomach is aching. It's a good feeling but it's bad too. She reaches up to touch her hair. A clump of strands come away in her hand. She absent-mindedly drops them on to the floor. It seems to her like everything is in fast motion. She has the power to stop all this but yet she doesn't. It's not really she who's in control anymore – it's something else.

It's already one o'clock; just another eight hours and she can go to bed, to oblivious unconsciousness, where she won't feel the pain or the hollow aches inside her ... and then she can start trying to get through the next new day.

Sometimes when she's alone she thinks how she'd just love to run to the fridge, take out some food and eat it. No guilt, no punishment. Just to eat the food without thinking of the calories or of how she'll have to sacrifice something else, without knowing she'll have to spend the next ten minutes with her head over the toilet bowl and tears running down her face.

It would be nice to do that. Just to eat, no guilt. But then she thinks of her reflection. She bends down and pinches some flesh and gets so angry. She gets so angry she thinks this should be the end of it. She's messed up everything. What's the point? she thinks. She just wants to be normal.

It's been so long since she last felt truly happy, not just pretending to be. It's been so long since she last had energy, since she's felt good. She can't remember what it's like to live happily without pain, palpitations, without the constant ache in her stomach and the pains in her back. So long that she thinks all this is normal. It's what life is for her. It's the way things are. It would be nice not to think about food all the time. Not to be constantly hungry, to be able to go out and eat and not just drink weak tea. It would be nice to feel good about herself.

She used to wear skirts all the time. That was a long time ago. Now they just collect dust in her closet. She won't throw them out, because she's going to be skinny even if it kills her. She'd like to be able to wear a short skirt and feel good, to throw out all her baggy trousers ... just to look and feel good ....

She feels so hungry now but she can't eat. She has to stop herself. Her head is still pounding and her hands are moving so fast, her stomach is begging to be nourished, to be coated in something other than liquid, to feel good, to feel full. She stands up. She needs some more cigarettes, no more diet tablets, no more appetite suppressants, no more laxatives.

She goes down to her room, trying to avoid the mirror. Then she takes her make-up and tries to cover the dark, sunken bruises under her eyes and the pale grey colour of her skin.

Afraid

Sinéad

Sometimes I just sit alone
So afraid to think
Afraid to come to terms with my own feelings
And my own thoughts

Afraid of the thoughts that go through my mind
Afraid to face reality
In case there's nothing ahead for me
Except the hatred and pain
That lies all around me.
Wherever I turn, there's another obstacle
That's so hard to get over
Maybe if I didn't try so hard
It would just make this world
I'm living in so much better
Sometimes I wonder if my feelings will ever change
Sometimes I feel there's nothing out there for me
Except all the confusion
That makes the world a bad place to live in
Always afraid of being let down
Always afraid of being refused
Afraid of not being accepted for the person I am
Afraid people won't understand the way I am
And the way I feel
Sometimes I wonder
Is it worth it all, this life I'm living
Or is it always going to be full of
Hurt, pain, hatred and confusion

THE BOXER

Catherine

The boxer went into the ring
tied his hands behind his back
put a blindfold around his head.
His opponent hit him again and again
'Why did you do that?' he said
but he still smiled as he bled.

The second time he stepped in to fight
he had his hands free
but he still couldn't see.
He thrashed around madly with all his might
'cos he knew he didn't like the pain
but his opponent gave him more of the same.
The fold was removed
and all was clear.
'I've shown what to do, there's no need to fear,
There's a much better place for me to be.'
He jumped out of the ropes and then he was free.

I CAN'T COPE ANYMORE

Helen

I can't cope anymore.
Why is life so difficult,
Full of sorrow and woe?
Things never seem to change
No matter now far down the road I go.
I try, boy, do I try so hard,
But like a little worm
I'm trampled in the mud,
And as usual have to start over again.
Why me? Please let the hurt stop.
I can't cope anymore,
No matter how hard I try.
Why, when so many people care,
Do I feel so alone?
Memories trapped in my mind
With nowhere to go but
Deeper and deeper inside the abyss.
Tears creep from my eyes

And are drained away
Only to be replaced by fresh ones
In this dull and sullen day.
Why is life so complicated?
No matter how hard I try
Things never change.
Where is all the happiness gone?
Why? Oh why? Has it slipped from my grip?
Is there any hope, behind the walls
Of this dark, deep and ugly pit?
Why me? Please let the tears drop.
I can't cope anymore.
Please let the last tear drop.

THE PERSON I WAS!

Nicola

The days feel so dark and empty
And the nights are long and lonely.
And as I lay in bed at night
I close my eyes with all my might.
And I think of the days gone by
When I hadn't got a worry in my mind
When I loved my body and myself.
But now I look at myself with disgust.
'I must lose weight, I know I must!'
My body fills me with a feeling of hate
Where once was a time, when I felt so great.
But life has gone slowly down
And the vicious circle keeps going round.
Every day is like the last, and many more are to pass.
It's emptiness and loneliness making me sad,
And the sight of my body making me mad.

How I'd love to like myself inside and out
And then I would be able to shout
That I am what I am, like it or not.
And I love myself.

DO YOU KNOW?

Emma

Do you know what it's like to look at your body and feel ill?

But that is no different because you are sick every day whether you make yourself or not.

Do you know what it is like to touch your skin and feel repulsed by the thick white flesh that's so normal to everyone but you?

Do you know what it's like to look at your fingers and see them getting fatter by the second?

Do you know what it's like to wake up thinking of food and know you can't have it and to go to bed guilty and happy with angry, stabbing pains in your stomach?

Do you have any idea of what it is like to force your already swallowed food out into the toilet 5, 6 or 7 times a day?

Can you imagine what it is like to feel your life slipping away when all you can think of is food, fat, vomit, pain and death?

If you do, then I understand; if you don't then you are so lucky and I wish I didn't either.

Success is getting up one more time than you fall down.

Thursday, 18 April 1968

My friend,

I am back to talk to you again. A lot of things happened from the last time I wrote to you. I had a horrible time. You just would not believe it. I was so desperate I did not want to live. I'm sorry I was not even able to write to you.

My parents played a trick on me. I still think it was only a horrible nightmare. I cannot even write about it. I am getting very upset. They took me to a doctor. First they said it was just for some tests for my sleep. I cannot sleep lately. Now I am sorry I told that to Mum, but then I discovered the visit was about my eating, because I had lost a lot of weight.

The doctor told my parents I might have an illness called 'anorexia'. They cannot even pronounce it properly. And she told them as well that I have to eat. So Mother keeps going on about not eating, saying that I have to eat or I will die, and if I do not eat I will go to hospital. I don't know which is the worst of the two. I was also given tablets which made me constantly groggy.

Dear friend, what will I do? What can I do? I'm desperate. I cannot eat but I have no choice. I do not want to destroy my parents' lives. I love them. Is there anybody out there that can hear me? Help me!

Marie

Friday, 10 May 1968

Dear friend,

Great news for you, friend. My plan is working and I am so glad I have you to share it with. Let me tell you how things are progressing. I have lost even more weight and I feel on top of the world. I'm so happy. Life is great. And this is only the beginning. The future is looking good. I've read my diet book several times. It goes everywhere with me. I've also bought more magazines. In fact, I may have gone overboard buying magazines. I can't get enough of them. They have become an obsession with me. What I do is, I gather all the information from them about diets and recipes and keep records of everything I eat.

Before Mother goes to work she prepares breakfast for me and sandwiches for school. I can get rid of all that food into the bin and in its place I have a grapefruit and a hard boiled egg and finish off with some black coffee to give me energy. More importantly the coffee kills my taste for food.

My parents never allow me to drink coffee, but I love it. I don't know whether it's the taste I like or the fact that I never feel hungry after having some. I carefully wash the cups afterwards and put them back in the exact place and hope my parents won't notice anything out of the ordinary.

I don't eat cakes or sweets anymore, though sometimes I feel weak and am really tempted. But in those moments my biggest help is to remember the pictures of beautiful models and to concentrate on how I will be as thin as them. That soon takes away my cravings and kills my appetite. Thankfully my willpower is getting stronger. It is not perfect, but it is getting better.

The evening meals are the most difficult. I have started making excuses to avoid eating with my parents. I might say that I have eaten earlier or that I had a big lunch. Sometimes Mother believes me and I get away with it. But more often than not I am caught and I have to eat under protest. It causes a lot of hassle. But I don't care. I'm becoming more determined. I want to lose weight, to be slim and beautiful. I won't finish her dinners even if they feed me like a baby. She has tried that but I refused to open my mouth. I don't care how angry she gets.

I have also discovered a new system of exercises. It's funny how things that you take for granted in the house can take on a whole new meaning. For example, the stairs. I had never really noticed how many stairs we had until now and how useful they could be!

When my parents are out I put on a T-shirt, track-suit and runners and run up and down the stairs. I start in the cellar, then the first floor, second floor and finish in the attic, and then all the way back down again. I do this again and again, each time faster and faster. It is hard work but it will be worth it. I am going to be happy. Running is the best exercise, because you are burning more calories. It is very hard work, but I am feeling the results. I love the feeling of physical exhaustion and the empty stomach grumbling from hunger. I feel excited, I feel high.

I am also becoming creative at making up recipes, for example 'scrambled egg white'. It consists of egg whites only, fried on a non-stick pan without any oil, of course. It does not taste the best, but who cares! It is full of vitamins and nutrients and most importantly it has almost no calories. The diet is costing me a fortune and I'm not sure how much more I can afford. I have to buy more coffee because my parents will notice that the coffee is disappearing. I buy the cheaper blend and mix it with Mother's more expensive one. I hope and pray they will not notice.

Anyway, there is loads happening at the moment. We'll talk again later.

Marie

Thursday, 13 June 1968

Dear friend,

I am back again. The situation is just a tiny bit better today. I did not put on any weight, thank God. I went back to school for a little while as I regained my energy. I absolutely hate my body, but I have no choice but to eat. It is very difficult to talk to my parents, so I stay in my room to keep out of the way and avoid any hassle. I just lie on the bed staring at the ceiling and dreaming that one day I will be famous, skinny and popular. But until that day I do not know what I'm going to do.

I must start exercising again. I have no choice. Yesterday we got my results from school. They were good and my parents were in good humour for a change.

'You see, Marie, you are clever. There is so much waiting for you. You must not destroy your life ...' and on and on Mother went with her lecture. I shut down and did not listen. I had heard it all before. But I must say in their defence they are making more of an effort to talk to me than I am to them and the nagging has eased off very, very slightly.

Earlier tonight I overheard a conversation between my parents. They are planning a holiday and the word 'anorexia' was mentioned. According to the doctors I need a change of air and location. They say that should make me better. Unfortunately I could not hear all the conversation and didn't understand much of what they were talking about. But to be honest I did not really care anyway.

Lately again I cannot sleep. The word 'anorexia' is playing on my mind and bothering me. What does it mean? Slimming illness. It is a strange word. They think I am sick with anorexia or whatever they call it. I'll have to find out more about it. Losing weight can hardly be an illness and if it is, I am so glad I have it.

Father cannot understand anyway. I can feel that, or maybe he does not want to know. He thinks it is more a madness than a disease, and that I should just pull myself together and start to eat. So they think the holiday will fix everything. What a 'magic holiday' it should be!

I'm looking at my figure in the mirror. All I can see is fat, fat and more fat. This will have to be got rid of before we start this 'magic holiday'. More exercises are necessary. More calories have to be burned off. First thing tomorrow my new regime will begin. I want to look really well for this holiday.

                                                                    Marie

You might lose the ideal but find the real.

4

A DAY IN THE LIFE OF...

In the description and treatment of people with eating disorders, there is a tendency to use a lot of labelling. It is time we started to question these labels put on people by others who have never experienced this condition. It is time we asked the people who are going through the condition. They are the real experts. We must ask them, 'How does life feel when your mind is eaten by negativity?' Hopefully, by reading this chapter you will learn more about these wonderful and misunderstood people. People are not 'anorexics' or 'bulimics' or 'overeaters'. Everybody is a unique and individual person. People with eating disorders are more than just a collection of labels. Sufferers can be any shape or size. What they all have in common is their hyper-sensitivity and the emotional suffering they go through. The more we learn to understand the way they feel and think, the more they can emerge from their shroud of secrecy and look for help.

THE TWILIGHT ZONE

Barbara

I don't think I've dealt with anything very well recently. See, I'm doing it again, responding to all the destructive garbage in my head. But I have not really dealt with things. If the truth be known I took on two jobs by my own choice and got so tired as a result of this undertaking that I was won over by my own inner demon. Have I have been so lost and felt so hopeless because of the mundane repetitiveness of my life, the lack of fun? I have chosen my life at present. Who can I blame but myself? I sure as hell do not want to go through each day in the 'twilight zone' or 'exile' that I have lived in for so many years.

I walked around town today like I had no right to be there. I was a scarlet woman. I'd binged for twelve days, a bender. I actually thought about going home again as I crossed O'Connell bridge. I was scared someone might look at me. Worse, someone might know me. I've never experienced that feeling as intensely as I did last week, returning to work after an absence of three days, doing you-know-what! I was walking up Grafton Street and a pounding began in my brain. Everyone was magnified a thousand times, all looking at me, knowing full well what was going on in my head. There it was written on my face for all to see. Oh God, somebody help. Actually no, go away, stop looking at me! Then it grew worse because I realised no-one was looking. 'Why not? What's wrong with me?' I managed to calm myself a little by remembering that other people are, themselves, too busy being paranoid and delusive.

Would I be let out if people knew the inner working of my brain? The battle continues, folks, with one persistent inner demon, for want of a better name. Then again, we all love names, labels, categories. It makes us feel safer in our beds at night.

Went to the cinema on Sunday and, yet again, all eyes were on me – so says the working of my wrecked young inner self. Give me a label I can work with here. I could hear their thoughts. 'Look, the recluse, the hermit married to exercise. She used to be bulimic/anorexic but she prefers anorexia because our western psyche is more accepting of a woman starving herself rather than forcing so much food into her stomach until she feels the stomach lining stretching then purges it all down a toilet bowl. Snap! Back to reality. Am I strange? Yes. I always was in ways. Everything is strange to us when we don't understand. Regardless of emotional suppression which I am recovering from in snakes and ladders fashion, what I'd love to do just for one day is, tell people exactly what I really think when they say something disrespectful or annoying to me, when I feel angry, resentful, sad, disagreeable, tired, confused, calm, joyful, strong, shy, irritated, lethargic, enraptured, happy, serene, lonely, insecure, hurt, deflated, hopeful, hopeless, constructive, destructive, alive, dead.

People would get a real shock to know what's really been going on up there in my noggin for so long. I'll tell you one thing. I did.

A Slice of Bread

Anita

I haven't eaten anything in two days. I'm planning to go for three. Yesterday I was dazed, disillusioned, out of reality. A zombie would be a word I would associate with how I am now. But today, I still don't eat. I can't. I don't want to. I am weak and tired. Sometimes I don't even have the energy to laugh, to walk from one room to the other or to even move my arms. When I walk down the street people don't look at me. They don't notice me anymore. I look pale, sick and withered. Not attractive. But I don't care. I have passed from craving food and just needing to eat, through to the stage of denying myself food with willpower no matter how much I want it or how hungry I am. I've suppressed my painful hunger pangs with diet coke and stuffed myself with coffee. I've resisted food no matter how much I want.

Now, today, I am at the stage of not being able to eat at all. Food doesn't interest me. I don't feel physical hunger anymore. I don't want food, and I don't eat it. I don't see how it will give me energy and nourishment. This is the stage I prefer, but it can only last for so long. People tell me I've lost weight. I don't know whether to believe them. I can feel my empty stomach between my protruding hipbones. My hands are limp and scaly. I looked in the mirror. My legs are still fat.

I have just eaten a slice of bread and broken the stage I was at. I have to get through the third day. I have eaten. What do I do now? Do I eat more? I don't want to but I crave food now because I have already eaten. Where do I stop? At least if I've eaten nothing, I've eaten nothing and I can resist eating. But if I've eaten, what do I do then? Why not eat more? I've nothing to strive for. Now I feel fat. I need to lose weight. I have to get rid of the fat on my thighs. I need to be thinner. I feel huge. Although, the funny thing is I don't look any different than I did before that slice of bread. I am still pale. My legs do feel fatter but couldn't possibly have changed. I still have scaly hands. People don't see me any bigger. But I feel huge, blown up with a fat stomach. These feelings cause me to eat more and the whole cycle starts again. And I will continue to strive towards these days when I am unable to eat.

A few days later, as I read over what I've written it sounds insane. But every word is the truth as to how I felt. To most, some people's obsession with food is ridiculous, incomprehensible, unnecessary, but to the person experiencing it it is a nightmare, a painful reality. Today I can say I ate a slice of toast for breakfast and didn't feel too guilty and I will continue to eat what I can for energy and health and try my best to get better. So there is hope. You can change and there is a way out of this torture. Even for me!

BULIMIC'S SECRET

Marie

Everybody admired her
The way she walked
The way she looked
But do they know?
Everybody envied her
The way she dressed
The way she smiled
The way she touched
But do they know?
They often asked her
How she does it.
She showed them, told them,
She helped them if they needed.
But she made sure, they never knew.
No, nobody can know
How the night can be so long
And the day can go slow,
And hopefully one day it will be all over,
But she has to make sure they will never know.

WHO HAS ALL THE ANSWERS?

Helen

Sick again
When will it end?
Why did it start
My fair-haired friend?
What can I do to make it stop?
If only I knew!
I try so hard but to no avail,
It seems to be reaching a larger scale.
Who has all the answers?
I'll never know.
Do I have much further to go?
This is no way for me to be,
Please, somebody set me free.
I hate myself for what I am,
Always sick – I wish there was calm.
Fat and tearful, lonely and sad,
Why must I be thin to feel glad?
Who really knows where the answers lie?
I hope to God I find out before I die.

A HAM SANDWICH

Anita

Why at 16 years of age do I feel so guilty and fat and so annoyed at myself for eating a ham sandwich? To the logical mind this sounds ridiculous, almost absurd, unthinkable. Yet to so many people this is normal. And it is only the tip of the iceberg. There is much worse to be experienced like the anger and disgust when you look in the mirror and grab the rolls of flesh on your body, the feeling of confusion you get right before you binge, the painful bloated feeling of your stomach expanded and packed with food, the embarrassment of returning to the shop again and again for more and more food, the pain of your throat and belly as you vomit up your sins and the starvation and frailty of your bones. The killing hunger pains that you endure at any cost just to be skinny. Please don't think that you are alone. You are not.

There are tons of people out there waiting to help you. Don't think that you don't have a big enough problem to get help. You don't have to make yourself sick 5 or 6 times a day or be 6 stone and fading away to have a problem. Others too feel confused and annoyed and trapped, almost hysterical with the pain and the self-hatred and self-disgust. I don't know what to say to you to make it better. I don't know what to say to myself. If there was some miracle cure I would have taken it by now, but there isn't. But that does not mean there is no cure, that there is no help, because there is and no matter how bad you think your problem is you can get better. Please don't waste any more of your precious life.

I started off just wanting to be thin and dieting and counting calories at the age of 11 and this progressed to more diet books, different methods, excessive exercise, bingeing, dieting, bingeing, dieting, exercising, losing weight, putting on weight and then starving, bingeing, vomiting, starving, bingeing, panic, thin, fat, thin, fat, thin. When I started to diet little did I know that this was just a symptom, that something else was wrong. In fact there was a lot wrong, but all I thought was that I was fat. Dieting was easier to occupy my mind with than what was actually happening at the time to me. I find here I am now trying to shut out the real reason. Don't diet, don't starve. Find the real reason you want to lose weight. Maybe the real reason is that you don't like yourself.

'Do what you can, with what you have, where you are.'
Theodore Roosevelt

Monday, 15 July 1968

My friend,

Life is fantastic. I have lost a good bit of weight. Even my friends have noticed and commented on it. 'Marie, you are very pale and thin,' they say. It is great to hear that. I love it. At long last I am getting the results I have worked hard for and I am really starting to enjoy it. I still have more weight to lose. My willpower is good and I do believe that soon I will be just as good-looking as the girls in magazines. One problem, though, and it's bothering me. My breasts are slowly getting bigger and noticeable. Even Mother remarked on them. I was so embarrassed. She has suggested we go shopping for a bra. No way! I do not want breasts and certainly no bra. I do not want to look like a grown woman yet. I am only thirteen and I will have plenty of time for all that.

I will have to put a stop to it. There must be a way to stop them growing. I feel desperate over the whole thing. How can this happen to me? The models in my magazines have hardly any breasts at all. I wonder how they manage to be nice and flat. I could not find information in my books about how they achieve that look. I guess I will have to exercise more to make them smaller. I hate them. There is a girl in my class and she has quite big breasts. I think she is wearing a bra already. She looks terrible. I cannot stand her, or her breasts. But mind you the boys seem to like her. She is very popular with them. They are always hanging around her. They do not seem to mind the fact that she is stupid. I do not like her, or the boys either, and I never will. I prefer to be on my own.

Something amazing happened last week. I was shopping with Mother when I saw some black and navy T-shirts, which I liked very much. I was in luck, and to my surprise Mother was in a generous mood. She bought both of them for me without any argument. I could not believe it. What shocked me even more, she said they suited me. I love them. I wear navy cord jeans with the navy T-shirt. I feel like a million dollars.

Another thing I have noticed lately is that I have more friends now. A few classmates have told me I look really well. You know, of course, that is because I am losing weight. I did not tell them about my dieting and exercising. No, that is our secret.

It has been hard work to achieve the way I look now and I intend to keep working at it. I know there is more hard work and annoyance ahead of me before I reach my goal. Anyway, I do not think my girlfriends or anyone would understand what I am trying to do. I cannot confide in any of them. So that is why I really need you, my friend. You are the one I trust with my secret. I always feel better when I have shared my problems, my downs, and my successes with you. I know you will not judge me, as others might do. Deep down I know I am crazy, but it is very important to me to look better. I want to be thin and skinny. I want to be happy.

Oh I nearly forgot! I have found another way of exercising, an easier way, and I am enjoying it. All I do is switch on the radio and I dance and dance to loud music. It's better fun than running up and down the stairs and I do not feel as tired. The music actually gives you energy and without realising it you are working harder, and burning away the calories. It's so easy. I wish I had thought of it before.

So, my friend, I'll sign off for now. We will talk soon.

Marie

Monday, 12 August 1968

My dear friend,

I'm so happy I have you with me. I have so much to tell you. We are having a great time. The place is absolutely beautiful. The villa we are staying in is right beside the sea. Everything seems so white. Not the ordinary white. This is a brilliant and shiny white. The sun is making it shine and it sparkles. The windows and doors are painted blue and everything looks like it is straight out of a fairytale book. The sitting room has a big window which opens out on to a balcony and every day you are greeted by the fresh sea air and gentle soft wind. I love it here.

Inside, the sitting room is papered in a lovely warm soft peach colour, with small white boats on it. This is the largest room in the apartment. From there we go into the kitchen which is quite small, all white with lovely blue handles on the presses. My parents have the big bedroom with their own bathroom. I have a smaller room but it has its own shower and toilet. There are two single beds in my room and some nights I sleep in one bed and the next night I might switch to the other, if it gets too hot. It's fun. I like change. This simple room has its own atmosphere and it's my little kingdom. From my window I can see the village and at night before I go to sleep I listen to the music floating up from the restaurants and cafés below.

The whole place reminds me of a scene from an old film. I can't believe that I am really here. I would love to stay here forever. I'm tanned and Mother says I look better, and for a change I find myself agreeing with her. I'm starting to like myself a little bit. My parents look happy too. We are having a lovely time together. At night we go for a walk around the bay and watch the fishermen taking in their catch, getting the fish ready for the market next day. Other times we go to the village to explore the shops and cafés and the little laneways between the houses. There is always something exciting and interesting to see no matter where we wander.

I'm eating, and I do not think I am putting on any weight. I now have to tell you a very big secret. I have made a fantastic discovery. I think I have solved my problem. I feel great about it. It is so simple. I wish I had thought of it before. From now on I am going to make everyone happy, especially me. It all happened a few days ago. In the village there is a market where local people sell their produce. Mother bought some savoury sausages, home-made of course. Well, they were gorgeous, spicy and juicy, completely different from the ones at home. The butcher said they were the local speciality. We cooked them for dinner and we all enjoyed them, but I found I could not stop myself eating and would have eaten them all, until I realised they had a minimum of 300 calories each and I had to stop myself and think about all the hard work I had done to get my figure the way it was now.

I could not throw it all away. But I was finding it impossible to resist the sausages. All that was on my mind was 'sausages, sausages and more sausages ...'

That night my parents went for a drink after dinner with a couple from downstairs. I did not go with them. I preferred to stay on my own, to read or listen to the radio. I enjoyed watching the night closing in and the moon chasing behind the clouds. I liked to listen to the sea, the waves beating on the rocks. The sea is so strong and powerful, I am fascinated by it. But what I was really trying to do was desperately distract myself from the one thought that kept coming back to me. Those stupid sausages. The craving was getting stronger and stronger and the more I tried to control it the more powerless I felt. Eventually I surrendered and left the scenery of the sea for the scenery of the kitchen. I forgot about my figure. I forgot all about calories and I decided to have a little party for myself. 'What the hell! I'm on holiday. I deserve to treat myself.' I had found an excuse for my behaviour. Just one sausage! After that I would not touch anything fattening for the remainder of the holiday. But right now I just had to have the sausages. I would swim and swim and do more exercises on the following day so as not to put on any more weight.

Even before I had started to eat I felt guilty. It was strange because after the first bite I forgot about everything. All I could think about was, what could I eat next? I started thinking, how can some people eat so much and remain slim? Why can't I eat what I want? It's just not fair. Suddenly I remembered my friend Anne. She was a girl who lived near us. She was always stuffing her face, yet never getting fat. I had always admired her figure and one day I asked, 'How is it, Anne, that you are so slim and yet you can eat as much as you want? Tell me, how do you do it?'

She pulled me nearer and whispered, 'It's easy, Marie, but you must not tell anyone. Promise me. It has to be our secret.' Well, she went on to describe how she eats and drinks what she wants and when finished goes to the bathroom, puts her fingers down her throat and all the calories are gone. It's as easy as that, she said. You simply eat and drink as much as you like, yet you remain slim the way you want. These words which at the time I was absolutely disgusted with now kept ringing in my ears. This was Anne's way of slimming. It was not mine. I didn't think it would ever be mine. I even started avoiding Anne because I thought what she was doing was revolting. But now things were different, because I had eaten another three sausages and the craving had still not gone.

That conversation kept hammering in my brain and in the end I decided to give it a try. It was worth an attempt. The idea put me in good humour. After all the starving and dieting it would be lovely to treat myself and fill my tummy again. And to know that I could get rid of all the calories in one go. I cooked the rest of the sausages, happy and relieved. I ate them one after another. How lovely it was not having to worry about calories. No counting. I forgot about everything around me. I was in heaven and I was free. What would I eat next? I really gorged myself. I ate some biscuits. It had been a long time since I ate a biscuit, but I really made up for it now. I then remembered there was some ice cream in the fridge. My favourite flavour. I really enjoyed my little party. I really needed this treat. Eating without worrying. It was fantastic. I'm starting to live.

My tummy by now was beginning to hurt me. I just could not eat anymore. That was okay, because there was not really much left in the food presses anyway. I sat back and relaxed and savoured the nice full feeling. I smacked my lips and wallowed in the moment before I took on my new slimming techniques. I would be lying if I said I was not afraid. I kept delaying what I had to do. I did not want to do it. But it was too late now. There was no turning back. The fear of getting fat was stronger than my fear of what I had to do next. The pain in my stomach was

getting worse, but it was only physical pain. Mentally I was free. I had
the answer. I did not need to be fearful of tomorrow. And even though I
was afraid of what I had to do, I was delighted with my new discovery.
This would make my parents happy. They could stop worrying about
my not eating. The answer to all our problems! The pressure of my little
party was getting worse and I could delay it no longer. I went to the
bathroom and dealt with the unfinished business. Everything had to be
done before mother and father returned.

I did it. It was not as hard as I had thought. Actually, it was quite
easy. A few unpleasant seconds and all was gone. Flushed away. I
cleaned myself, brushed my hair. It was all past history. I looked in the
mirror. I could see a slim, beautiful, fantastic me. After a while I went to
bed and slept like an angel. I was so pleased with myself. I did not even
hear my parents come home.

Next day Mother was looking for the remainder of the sausages. 'I
ate them,' I piped up. 'I was hungry.' 'Oh that's wonderful, darling,' said
Mother with a smile on her face, and then she was hugging and kissing
me. It felt good. It had been a long time since Mother had hugged and
kissed me or even put her arms around me. I had often wanted her to do
it, to be her baby again, her little girl. But I could never get the courage to
do it. It was lovely to see her smile and look happy. It had taken so little
to make that happen. Anne's plan had worked after all. It had been a
great discovery – look at all the happiness it had brought! From that
moment the holiday really took off. The pressure was off all of us now.
We relaxed and really enjoyed ourselves. I started to eat all kinds of food.
The fear was gone. Anything and everything that was put in front of me
I ate. To the amazement of my parents I even asked for second helpings. It
was a blessing that I had my own bathroom and nobody could disturb
me or interfere with my new slimming methods.

One of the days on holidays I was strolling around the village on my
own. I was happy and content. I saw an ice-cream parlour. My eyes
nearly fell out of my head. I had arrived in heaven. There in front of me

were different-flavoured ice creams, orange, lemon, vanilla, strawberry and almond chocolate. My mouth was watering. The temptation was too strong. In I went and had a double portion of everything. There was no stopping me now. Later, on my way back to the villa, I came upon a shop which had lovely cakes and thought to myself, 'Why not?' And I went ahead.

Life is so much easier for me now, now that I have discovered this new slimming method. It's strange eating anything I like, because for so long I was denying myself everything. It's a different feeling. I feel high. I can't explain it, because I never felt like this before. Before I was always watching and fighting with myself. But this is different, completely different. I'm eating and my parents are happy; everybody is off my back. Of course I do not like the part of having to get rid of the food. I have told myself, 'Marie, you have to pay for everything in life; there is never a free ride; everything has a price.' I feel I am getting this very cheaply. I will try not to dwell on it too much and not make a big deal out of it. It only lasts a few minutes. One long minute and then everything is gone ... gone ... gone.

Marie

One can stand still in a flowing stream,
but not in the world of men. Japanese proverb

5

COPING SKILLS FROM THE CHEMIST

Conclusive statistics about the extent of laxative abuse are virtually impossible to find. Because of the factor of shame, it is difficult to get the actual figures, yet we can only imagine it to be much higher than people realise. Experience of working with people would suggest that the taking of laxatives is extremely common.

Laxatives can give us a very false feeling of slimness or of lightness, but the reality is that what we lose is not weight but health. Taking laxatives in any form can become addictive. Overcoming this dependency is very time-consuming and requires a lot of determination. It is very important that attention is paid to laxative abuse as early as possible in recovery.

LAXATIVE ABUSE

- ◊ When you are taking more than twice the recommended dose at least once a week for more than 3 months, then we are talking about laxative abuse.

- ◊ A laxative is any product designed to stimulate evacuation of the bowels. It can appear in tablet, syrup, salt or drink forms.

- ◊ You need to realise that laxatives do not have an effect on weight control. Most food is absorbed in the small intestine, while laxatives work on the large one, so it is already too late for them to act.

- ◊ Most food sufferers feel better after taking them, because they get rid of the sensation of being bloated. However, this effect weakens as the habit grows. Laxatives only give the illusion of weight loss, by causing dehydration through the loss of body fluids. This can cause a lot of health problems.

- ◊ If you are using laxatives, remind yourself that they do not have any effect on the body's fat levels. Keep reminding yourself that you lose only your health and dignity.

- ◊ When coming off laxatives, do it gradually. Make a chart or your usage and go easy at first. Cut down the doses and try to keep some days 'laxative free'. Ask yourself what makes you want to take them. Look for other options.

- ◊ If possible throw away all packets. Try not to keep them in the house and remind yourself that your stomach will feel less bloated after giving up laxatives. Focus on the positive side. If possible, ask for support!

Tuesday, 5 October 1971

Dear friend,

Me again. This honestly is not the best time of my life, but I am trying very hard to cope. Maybe it would be better to say that I am existing and living in hope, and, more importantly, I am trying to settle this mess I am in. Since I talked to you last and promised you that I would never go back to my crazy ways, I have been trying very hard to eat normally, alas with not much success. I either eat like a savage or eat nothing at all. I can't seem to reach a happy medium. I can't go without food for a long time anymore. Some voice is saying to me, 'Go on, treat yourself, Marie. This will be the last time.' I try to convince myself that after each little 'treat' it will be the last time. But it never seems to work out like that. The more I eat the hungrier I become and then I eat anything I can get my hands on. For a while I feel fantastic, life is a breeze and so manageable and nothing bothers me. Everything bad is forgotten. Then comes the feeling of being too full. I start thinking about tomorrow when I have to go to school and face my friends and I must look slim. I have no choice. I cannot keep all this food inside me. I have to go back to my old plan. Then desperation sets in. I persuade myself that this will be the last time. I try to block everything out of my mind. 'No more' has to be my aim. But I know I am a failure and that it's impossible to reach it. 'Last time' is now becoming 'once more'.

I'm looking for important dates to help me motivate myself, but again it seems the more effort I put into it the greater the failure I become, and the feeling of guilt is overwhelming. I know I am destroying myself. This madness is going on too long. Please God help me and bring me this 'new tomorrow' when I can become a normal person again. I do not understand myself anymore. One minute I am so depressed and I don't know what to do, and then again I can become the biggest optimist in the world. I'm up and down like a yo-yo. But I honestly do believe that one day I will be normal and that my 'new tomorrow' is coming. Then this food horror will be forgotten and be behind me.

Oh, I nearly forgot to tell you something really important, Mother is great for collecting different types of herbs. She picks the herbs, dries them out, and combines various flowers and herbs to make different types of tea and remedies. When they are all prepared she keeps them in jars in the cupboard with little stickers on them which describes the contents of each and what illness or disorder they will help. Lately my interest in the herbs has increased. I do not know why I went to the cupboard that evening, but the first jar I spotted, it seemed almost to jump out at me and the label read 'Constipation'. I suddenly remembered what I had read recently in biology class. If people suffer from diarrhoea, the food is not properly digested and because of this the food leaves the body quicker and the person loses a lot of weight rapidly.

I began to think and play with the idea that maybe if I drank a lot of this tea I could manage to lose a few pounds this way. Maybe with this new plan I would not be needing my old system of slimming and I could forget that part of my horrible past. I got very excited. I was dying to try it. I could not wait until my parents went for their evening walk. Then I could pour myself a cup of that magic tea.

When eventually they left, the moment arrived and I had the house to myself. First I boiled the kettle, opened the cupboard and gingerly took out the important jar. When I removed the lid the stench hit me like a boulder; it reeked. The smell was horrible and overpowering. 'Relax, Marie, this is going to work,' I told myself. 'Hold your nose, forget the smell and think of the results. Get moving. You don't have much time.'

I poured a little water into the teapot and spooned in the herbal tea. I waited a little while to let it set. Mother said it should be left for about five minutes. So while waiting I did some exercises. The tea was soon ready. The smell was really dreadful. But I knew I had no choice. I had to drink it. I had already eaten more than I should have, and I had to get rid of the calories. There is nothing I would not do to have a beautiful figure. I closed my eyes and then proceeded to drink the awful concoction. In fact I polished off the whole pot.

'God, I am crazy!' I was laughing to myself and enjoying my little secret. I embraced the high I was experiencing and I was so looking forward to the results. I hoped I would not have to wait for long. I was expecting results immediately and found it difficult to sleep that night. Nothing happened. In the morning I woke up very disappointed. I jumped straight up on to the weighing scales. 'Oh God help me!' I nearly died. I had put on almost a pound in weight. I started to cry and hysteria took over. I didn't feel like going to school. I didn't want to face anybody. But I had to. Today we were doing important exams. I was in a state. I didn't know what to do. I tried my best to calm myself. It was a hard job but eventually I decided to go to school.

I had a fantastic breakfast. It consisted of a double helping of Mother's tea. You know me, I never give up or do things by half. I had to lose a couple of pounds. I felt the tea would probably work when I came home from school. I had it nicely worked out, or so I thought. How wrong I was. During geography class I started to get pains in my stomach. I did not mind too much. At least there was now some reaction. The pains were soon getting stronger and stronger. I had not planned on this happening. They got sharper and sharper until I could no longer stand it. I had to excuse myself and leave the room. This happened a couple of times during the day. I was very embarrassed. As a result I missed half of the exams. My teacher was not impressed. 'Marie, you will have to resit the exam some afternoon on your own, when you are feeling better, of course. You are obviously not well and look very pale. You'd best go home ...'

Home I went. I was very thankful to her for excusing me because by this stage I was very weak. My legs felt like jelly. But boy was I happy! I now had another crutch. This new plan was working.

I know I have to control my intake of tea and cut down on the dosage. But I am so sure I'm going to lose weight this way! Not only am I getting rid of the calories, but I don't feel like eating. This magic tea is brilliant.

Marie

Friday, 12 January 1973

Dear friend,

How good it is to have you to fall back on. I am feeling so lonely and isolated. I miss having someone to talk to about how I am really feeling inside. Nobody can understand the mess I am in and I want to shout out loud and tell the world about my problem. If I could tell someone about the way I feel it might help. Just to unload it off my chest. It's suffocating me. I know I should not complain as I always have you to turn to. You have never failed me. Our relationship has been great. The longest and best I've ever experienced. You are the only one I can trust. It is because you do not answer back or criticise. You always listen.

Another year has gone by and I am still fighting my food, still trying diets. At this stage I know so much about diets and calories I could fill a library with them. Lately also I am planning my own diets. Every day I make out a special sheet giving details of the amount of food I allow myself to eat and the exact time I am supposed to eat at. Every morsel of food has to be weighed, balanced and within the calorie allowance. I follow my programme for about a week and then because I get so hungry and fed up, I abandon my special sheet, and run like a sprinter to the kitchen and eat everything in sight. These times I do not care about being fat or thin. The need to fill my stomach is greater and I give in again.

I do not always get rid of the food in the usual way. Yet again I am a failure. That side of the slimming is depressing me more and more. It is so humiliating. It is insane. Making myself sick is making me mentally sick. I stand, locked in the bathroom with the radio on and the taps running to disguise the noise and make sure no one hears me and suspects what I am up to. I feel so disgusted with myself and hate myself for doing it and not being able to stop, and so help me God it just seems to get worse and worse. I am getting nowhere and going round and round in circles. I have got away with it for so long but at some stage in the future I am bound to be found out.

Do you remember Mother's magic tea? Well, I have finished all her supply and for some reason she did not make any for a while. I wonder did she suspect what I was doing. So my new plan involved going on my own to the chemist as I knew for a fact that the local shop did not sell the tea.

Even though I was embarrassed asking for it, I had to have it. I needed it. The need was so strong it outweighed my embarrassment. Unfortunately the chemist did not have in stock the tea I required, but he very helpfully recommended a tablet that would meet my needs. This was great news for me. I had never realised before that you could take tablets. That would be easier than drinking that awful concoction.

'Which type would you like?' I didn't even realise that there were different tastes. Another discovery, another crutch. I am learning all the time.

'It doesn't really matter. Any will do, once it does the job. It's for my granny, a strong one, please.' I lied. The chemist was still talking. 'I think this one,' he said, handing me a packet. 'It is the best. Just one tablet at bedtime. They are really strong.'

There were sixty tablets in the packet. I didn't even bother to read the instructions. This pack would keep me going for some time. They were yellow tablets. Strange that such a small tablet could be so strong. I decided I'd better read the instructions and see if it did really say one only. Yes it did, and it also said the tablet must be taken at bedtime. The problem was I had had a big treat before I went to the chemist and I was anxious to get rid of the food. All the biscuits, ice cream, crisps and junk I had eaten I really needed to get rid of. I could not wait until bedtime to take the tablets. I decided to take four tablets straight away. I had to get rid of everything, and now!! This method of dieting seemed to be the easiest way of doing that.

I waited patiently, wondering how long it would take for the tablets to work. Two hours later cramps started and soon afterwards I got terrible diarrhoea, which lasted right through the day and into the night. I didn't mind. I would have the next day free and I was prepared to do anything to get rid of the poisonous calories. I felt great even though I was in terrible pain and discomfort. For the first time in a while I could feel my stomach beginning to flatten. I was thrilled with that. So for the next few days I ate fruit and drank only black coffee for energy. I was feeling quite weak after the laxatives. But I could easily handle that. It was much better than feeling fat so I put up with the pain.

The object of this exercise is to lose a little bit of weight. I really believe it will make a great difference to my life. I just want to be thin. I need to be thin. I know that everything will change for the better if I lose weight. I know I am crazy. I know normal people can eat, then stop when they have had enough. I cannot do that. I overeat, I then starve myself or get rid of it. Each time I touch food I just go crazy. I just have to have more and fill the enormous hole inside me. I do not understand why I am doing it. I hate to think too deeply about why I do it because I then become very depressed again. So hopefully this new discovery will be an answer. I do hope so.

Marie

> To live with the world around me, I must learn to live well with the world within me.

6

FESTIVE OR FURTIVE?

Christmas is supposed to be a time of joy, something to be looked forward to, yet for food sufferers it is a time of fear, panic and dread. It can be very frightening.

Food is an important feature of Christmas. It is a time for mince pies, cake, Christmas dinner. The emphasis on food is so great around this time that sufferers dread it. There are steps that can be taken to help decrease the amount of worry and fear a sufferer experiences in the run-up to Christmas.

This chapter is important in increasing the awareness of how a sufferer feels about this festive time. Remember ... awareness creates understanding and understanding creates hope.

CHRISTMAS AND A FOOD PROBLEM

Christmas is supposed to be the season of peace, happiness and joy. For many people it can be exactly that but for those who suffer from an eating disorder this happy season is a nightmare, a time of fear and dread as it draws nearer. This day their greatest fear is realised, the day the family members put on a positive face, sit down to eat together, relax over a meal and enjoy it. All this when what you really want to do is run away from it all.

For other family members there can be nothing worse than seeing a person you love trying desperately to destroy herself or himself, and knowing that there is nothing you can do about it. It is torture to see people literally starving themselves, or bingeing and vomiting. When one family member has a pain which manifests itself in physical symptoms, all family members end up feeling this pain in some way.

Experience of working with people who suffer from food distress shows up clearly how many people are afraid and are panicked well in advance of Christmas. This situation comes from thinking about the Christmas dinner, so much food and so much temptation, and the pressure of looking well at Christmas: 'the happy family', 'what will we wear?', and 'what is going to fit us?' Whether you are anorexic, bulimic, a compulsive overeater, or simply don't have the body you want, the emotional suffering is the same in nearly every case.

If you are a food sufferer, here are a few suggestions which can help you survive Christmas.

~ Do not expect a miracle.

~ Do not go on a starvation diet before Christmas just to fit into some dress or to 'look good' at that party.

~ Learn to relax and take it easy – avoid last-minute shopping.

~ Do not worry about having the same disastrous Christmas as last year. Every year is different.

~ Do not put too much pressure on yourself.

~ Talk gently to yourself.

~ Think of the nice things you could do and enjoy.

~ Nurture yourself – be nice to yourself.

~ Ask for help if you need to.

~ Live in the present.

~ Accept yourself.

~ If you have a setback, take it as a learning experience.

~ Be kind to yourself.

~ Never forget Christmas is only one day in the whole year!

It can often help if we plan how to cope with the holidays and ask ourselves how we want to feel. Many people find the following six guidelines helpful:

~ Be realistic. As long as you concentrate on everything going perfectly the more chance there is of things going wrong. Don't expect yourself or anyone else to be perfect.

~ Be flexible. Allow yourself to try new foods, even if only in very small amounts.

~ Take responsibility. You have control only over your own thoughts and actions, not over those of others.

~ Think positively. You get what you expect, so believe that things will go well. They more than likely will.

~ Be prepared to say 'no'. Prepare yourself to be able to decline food that you know you are not ready to handle yet. Think of ways to do this that will least offend, but don't put yourself under any pressure.

~ Prepare your family. The best way to help everyone to cope is to talk to your family before Christmas day. Help them to understand the pressure you feel. They will more than likely be glad you have talked to them.

Ask always: 'Is there a better way?'

A POEM FOR CHRISTMAS

Barbara

Christmas time
Let the yuletide ring
All the happy faces sing,
Carols old and carols new
Then there are the others too
For them it is a harrowing time
Watching others eat and drink wine
Fear to eat a single bite
Others long to eat all night
Food to them suppresses pain
You might say 'should be ashamed'
But the shame it is misplaced
When you turn your shameful face
Listen up and listen well
Christmas time for them is hell
So this season we express
We are many with eating distress
Men and women, girls and boys
Treated like unsavoury toys
It is true, yes it is real
Though the media try to conceal
Growing numbers day by day
Is this now the Irish way?

'Experience is not what happens to you; it is what you do with what happens to you.' Aldous Huxley

Saturday, 15 December 1973

My friend,

I have not written to you for so long. The time goes so fast. Recently things have not been so bad for me. But not the greatest either. Soon it will be Christmas. It depresses me. Everybody is in good humour and making others happy. Funnily enough I love to see other people happy. I still have not presents for my parents because I just do not know what to get them. It has to be something very special this year, especially for Mother, to show her how much I love her. Relationships between us at the moment remind me of a boat in a rough sea, up and down, bouncing all over the place. I know she is not proud of me. I am sure she would prefer if I was different.

It seems Mother is never satisfied with what I do. She wants things done her way all the time. Her way is always the best way. At school I do okay. I am not number one, but I always manage to keep in the top three. Yet Mother always reminds me, 'It would be nice if we had a better report from school. You have the ability, I know, Marie. You can do better.'

I don't care if I am first, second or third. I think sometimes I am going to school to please my parents, just for them to say to their friends what a smart and intelligent daughter they produced.

Sometimes I wonder if she loves me. Oh I feel guilty if I think like this. I know she loves me. At least I think she does, though I cannot remember her once telling me so. Maybe I have just forgotten. She appears quite cold and distant. I really would love her to hug and kiss me like I was her baby and for her to tell me that I am special. I know it is only a dream. I'm too old for it anyway.

This Christmas I promised to myself I am going to try to be the best daughter they could ever wish for. I'm going to help Mother a lot around the house and with the cooking. I will try not to answer back. I know she absolutely hates that. But sometimes she really drives me to it. This Christmas I will keep my mouth shut and do what I am told. The answer I would like to give will be kept in my head and as the old saying

goes, 'The less said the easiest mended.' I know it is not going to be easy,
because mother is always too ready with her own advice, and never
listens to anyone else. But, I will be a good listener and a good diplomat.
And I will become a model daughter.

Here I am waffling on about my problems and still have not solved
the problem of what I am going to buy them for Christmas that will
show I do love them.

I am too tired to think anymore. I will leave it until later. Goodnight,
dear friend. Thanks for listening.

Marie

Tuesday, 8 January 1974

Dear friend,

Here I am again whinging, moaning, complaining and being so unhappy.
I was putting so much hope into a new beginning. I wanted the New Year
to produce a new me. Over the Christmas, my food problem was again a
torture. Whenever I touched food I could not stop myself. I had promised
myself that the big day would be the 1st of January. It would be a new
start for me. I had plans to sort myself out. I was actually looking
forward to it. I had allowed myself to break all the rules. I treated myself
because I knew the new regime I had ahead of me was going to be a hard
battle. I felt I deserved a little treat because in the New Year it would all
have to stop.

The first and second days were okay. I just did not eat. Anytime I felt
hungry I kept reminding myself and repeating, 'Now, Marie, you can't. It
is a new beginning ... it is a new start, a new life ...' It was not easy. By
the third day I was really up against it. My parents had gone out for the
evening to visit friends and the moment they closed the door I was into
the kitchen like a bullet out of a gun. I was now a different person. It was
almost as if I had forgotten who I really was. I cannot explain it and

really I didn't care. I was like a wild animal. I'm so ashamed of myself and so very confused. I could not stop. So much for my good intentions and plans for the New Year. Everything gone in seconds! As a last resort, I told myself, I could always use my old slimming methods. I'm a dreadful, disgusting person.

What is happening to me? Where is it going to finish? It is never going to end. God, if only someone could help me. I will have to wait for another year to start my big day. I feel desperate and want to cry, scream and shout out loud, but I can't. Is there anybody out there who knows what this monster is doing to me. I want to be normal!

If I only knew there was somebody else who had the same problem! How do they manage to live with this monster? How do they cope? I'm so desperate and depressed. I have never felt so low. I wish I was dead.

I know I must be destroying my body. I have noticed lately that after each binge, when I use my way of getting rid of the calories my body starts to shake, my hands become sweaty, I lose some vision in my eyes, and I feel dizzy. These bouts last about an hour and it has become quite difficult to stop them. I know I am completely out of control, though I have discovered that taking a couple of cubes of sugar and several glasses of water can help. But not all the time. The worst part is that I never know when the attack is going to happen. It can happen two minutes after I get rid of the food, or it can happen two hours later. It is so unpredictable. It has happened when my parents are at home. Then I make myself scarce and hope it goes unnoticed.

I'd better tell you what else happened before I became even more depressed. A couple of days ago, Father took me with him on a business trip. The idea behind it was that the change would do me good. In almost every town we visited I went and had a look at the churches. I love going to churches. This day I discovered a really nice church. It seemed old and run down but there was something nice and peaceful about it. I felt a calm about me. I was composed and peaceful. Suddenly I spotted a light over a confession box and almost instantly my conscience was saying, 'Go

on, Marie, you will feel better. You need to tell someone about Christmas.'
As had happened before, one part of me wanted to go in, the other did
not. What would I say to the priest?

Suddenly I got a powerful urge to talk to someone. I could not keep the
secret inside anymore. Before I realised what I was doing I was kneeling
down. What I was hoping for was that he might understand and be able
to help me. Suddenly I was again filled with hope and elation. It was just
me and the priest. I was sure that if I poured out my heart to the priest I
would relieve myself of this unbearable guilt. I was willing to bare my
soul. I was tense and very nervous. My throat was dry and my chest was
hurting. Will I? Doubt was setting in. But the hatch suddenly opened. I
could not run now. The priest started to speak. I tried desperately to
remember some prayers and string some words together - anything that
made sense. I was looking for help from this priest. I spluttered out,
'Father, I wasted a lot of food.' There was a long pause. It was agony, I
tried to ease the silence by spluttering away. By now I didn't know what I
was saying. I ended up saying, 'I am sorry for what I am doing.'

Still nothing. No response. I began to wonder if he was there at all. At
last the silence was broken and I heard, 'Never mind, little one. Try not to
do it again, and say three Hail Marys.' I was stunned and speechless,
shocked. I was full of shame, disgust, and hate for myself. I ran from the
confessional and out of the church and did not stop until I was completely
breathless. I was afraid he might come out of the box and see who I was.
I realised my visit to the church was a disaster. Strangely enough, later
that evening I felt some inner peace for a while.

So as you can see, my friend, another Christmas, another New Year,
and I am still where I was. Where do I go from here?

                                                            Marie

Achieving starts with believing.

7

I USED TO BE A FITNESS QUEEN

Over-exercising is a common feature in many of the variations of eating distress. You don't need to be in the gym to misuse exercise. The urge to exercise often comes after eating and during periods of stress and tension. It's difficult to recognise this problem to its full extent because of the great emphasis on fitness in our times. This emphasis can be used as a means of covering up the real extent of the issue.

Over-exercising can be as difficult a habit to break as any other physical symptoms of eating disorders.

THE FITNESS ERA

We are living in the fitness era, the 90s. We are encouraged to eat low-fat food, increase exercise and reduce food intake. But what leads to good health?

We know that competitive athletic programmes may increase eating distress. Sportspeople of either sex are vulnerable. When the personality profile is one of high achievement and perfectionism, the combination may be lethal for individuals who base self-assessment on achievement. Female athletes, dancers, gymnasts, for example, are often willing to tolerate pain, ignoring fractures, torn ligaments and loss of their menstrual cycle in order to achieve their goal.

Food becomes the enemy instead of an avenue to enhance health and performance. Exercise becomes the means of purging calories and negative emotions. Exercise takes on a different meaning for some and may become a socially acceptable type of purging that receives partial reinforcement from family and friends. As the amount of exercise increases we may see food intake and appetite suppressed. A powerful sense of concealment develops. Sometimes it is necessary to stop exercising in order to determine if it is a problem. After about two days and maybe sooner, the person addicted to exercise may experience physical and psychological withdrawal symptoms:

~ confusion
~ lack of concentration
~ irritability
~ anxiety
~ panic attacks with hyperventilation
~ poor circulation
~ depression
~ suicidal tendencies

~ decreased energy

~ insomnia

~ lower confidence; loss of self-esteem.

In order to overcome the obsession, one must learn to talk about and express feelings in a healthy manner rather than use the body to numb or vent unpleasant feelings and escape reality.

A person with an exercise obsession will answer Yes to more than half of the following:

◊ Do I pass up social activities and spending time with family and friends to work out?

◊ Do I schedule my day around my exercise routine rather than my exercise routine around my schedule?

◊ Do I use exercise as a means of controlling food intake, of burning calories, of losing weight, as opposed to having fun, enjoying body movement, maintaining physical and emotional health?

◊ Is exercise a way to purge myself of unpleasant thoughts and bad feelings rather than expressing them?

◊ If I miss a workout, do I feel an increase in negative anxiety towards myself; am I stressed out, guilty, feeling fat?

◊ Do I determine how much exercise I will do in terms of how much food I've eaten?

◊ If I miss a work-out do I deny myself food?

◊ Do I ignore injury, fatigue and pain?

◊ Can I feel sensations in my body such as tiredness, muscle strain, tension?

◊ Is my body size always on my mind?

◊ Do I think about exercise all the time?

◊ Do I get a rush of energy from strenuous exercise?

LOOKING IN THE MIRROR

A. M. McG.

I look in the mirror and what do I see?
An image of someone I might call me
I see all the bad points clear to me
And I wish I was happy with all that I see.
I notice my nose a bit too fat
And my head is a bit too big for a hat
My hair is so fine
It's unfortunate that it is mine.
I'm not very happy, I'll have you know
But I realise that no-one is perfect, so,
No matter my shape, or colour or size
Or even if I feel fat inside
What Jesus sees, is a wonderful start
To a person restored by a change in her heart.

MONA LISA

Barbara

Can't you sit still? It won't take long, just a touch more shading and I can't go wrong. Could you try leaning forward? Show a few more smiles, stick your chest out, dearie. Give me big brown eyes.

If you'd hold your breath for a second or two. Oh that's great bone structure; this is really you. Won't your friends be jealous of this canvas and oil! When you're rich and famous, no more sweat and toil.

If you open a few buttons, maybe one or two, this is art pure and simple, and I'm doing it for you. Now you look all pensive, okay, keep your clothes on, but for pity's sake smile or that 'essence' will be gone.

Yes I know you're not happy. You think I'm a bloody wretch, but I'm exhibiting the painting and preliminary sketch. It's a cruel game, Mona, but someday you'll realise that they only like a painting with bare cleavage and big smiles.

THE EXERCISE OBSESSION

Barbara

As a long-time sufferer from bulimia and exercise obsession, I have many critical thoughts about the society in which we live. I am amazed, for example, at the amount of advertising for alternatives to conquering addictions, to becoming 'at one with yourself' (just ten minutes, twice a week, for £21.99). People everywhere want the same thing. We are all reaching a higher state of awareness now that we realise our cars, money, jobs and partners are not filling the void within us. Admitting this to ourselves is initially devastating. What's even worse is to ignore the realisation and carry on as before in the hope we will forget.

I myself tried for so many years to treat the behaviour as the main issue, the problem in itself.

This got me nowhere. I suddenly began to realise that my perceptions of the world, from within the mode of thinking I was stuck in, were not necessarily true or based on fact. I began to question my reason for self-destructiveness, for self-loathing. I began to question my opinions, my beliefs, my code of ethics. If I was perpetuating past experiences then my way of thinking was the culprit.

I never even considered exercise a problem until recently. It's so acceptable to over-indulge in it in the nineties in an effort to look better. We accept ourselves more if we're training in a gym seven days a week and eating cabbage leaves. I got caught up in the whole physical appearance gimmick when I started training obsessively in gyms from the age of 17. My experience tells me that men and women who are very unhappy within themselves, desperately trying to feel a level of self-worth, work to train their bodies and curb their thoughts until they are a person they can almost bear to be.

At the height of my physical addiction to exercise I was training every day. I weight-trained for a minimum of two hours a day, ran on treadmills and took aerobics classes before heading home to the realisation of facing food. Some nights I made myself sick two or three times, then got up the next morning to burn off any imaginary fat I'd put on. Now I know I was suffering from obsession. I needed help. Yet I was envied and congratulated for my madness. When I told one of my childhood friends of my psychological/physical addiction to exercise she replied, 'I wish I was addicted to exercise, then I'd be able to do something about my weight.' From where I was standing it seemed as though people wanted me to perpetuate the problem ... it was expected of me. That was how they 'related' to who they thought I was, so therefore there was no problem.

People still haven't realised that exercise can be equally as damaging as bulimia. It takes over your life and controls you from morning to night. I became addicted to the chemicals in my body. But the truth of it was, I wore my worth on my sleeve. How I looked dictated how I felt about myself. That's pretty unfair when you consider it because people who hate the way they look are always going to find fault with themselves and therefore have zero self-worth, no self-esteem, no mercy on themselves.

I see bulimia and excess exercise as a balancing act, one controlled by the other. When I trained I found it easier to live with myself even if I was continuously trying to reach a point I could never reach. That is the vicious circle. I used to say, 'When

I look like that I'll be happy.' But you never even 'see' the way you really look because the cards are all stacked against you. You're too busy hating yourself to look beyond the hypocritical fallacy of self-image.

Physically, there are very severe repercussions from exercise obsession. Firstly, the body/mind connection is broken; the person is unable to feel sensations, even pain from burns or cuts. I couldn't feel tiredness, tension, pain, exhaustion, even though it was evident. I didn't respond to my body's messages for rest or repair. I couldn't relax. This doesn't sound ominous, I know, but to witness me in periods of hypertension such as these was almost as exhausting to others. Insomnia, headaches, training injuries, physical wear and tear on the body eventually catches up. It caught up on me. I took painkillers to numb my aching head so that I could continue my work-outs. I constantly walked at high speed for five/six hours in the hope that I was burning bodyfat. I then started taking sleeping tablets to try and sleep. I wanted to numb bad patches from my consciousness. Many times I fought the urge to swallow the entire packet. My periods stopped for a long time. I was happy enough about this as it meant my bodyfat was below normal, but it still wasn't low enough for my liking.

Slowly but surely I've pulled back from exercise. This has been extremely difficult and painful for me. The weighing scales on occasion tilts in the other direction and I eat, binge and vomit, or eat and exercise for dear life. To others around me this is hard. I now realise this and often I feel guilt or shame on account of them. Sexuality, relationships and my family are issues I never really thought about but now I strive to accept my family as they are; whether they accept me or not is unimportant. I want to fully recover for myself now. I have tasted inner peace, sampled contentedness, and I want more. It has been said: 'Life itself is the binge.'

Sexuality is something I never contemplated being affected, but of course who we are as people applies to our sexuality too. Self-acceptance and sexuality are halves of the same whole. I want to love and be loved, give and receive love and have a special person to share every day with. I look around me and see the dependency of so many relationships, the needy insecurities of our childhood never being resolved, and affecting our relationships as adults. The easy thing to do is to fall into a person's arms and expect to be happy. Of course I know that what we deny to ourselves will colour everything we partake in. Basically, if you aren't happy by yourself then how on earth can you be happy with anyone else?

I want to be patient and grow out, take root and flower with the right someone. Timing is the question here. Do I wait until the day I'm completely at one with myself? That said though, when will it be? And what of the bad days? I feel less empowered and less inclined to reach out, but it's imperative that I do. It's so easy to recoil into the inner world where no one can reach you. But to stay outside and want support and interaction with others ... well it's a step in the right direction.

The reason I discuss relationships here is because no matter what the stage of your recovery, you need someone to talk to, to cry to. Hiding on your own in your bedroom doesn't mean you're braver. Quite the opposite. I have found it more difficult to open up my pain with others when I've felt particularly bad, yet knowing I can has somehow made me feel stronger.

You cannot have a perfect body, only a perfect feeling about the body you have.

8

MALE SUFFERERS

*Because of the fact that this condition is often mistakenly
viewed as a teenage girl's problem, it can be extremely difficult
for male sufferers to be open about their illness and to look for
help. The stigma attached to this condition is greater for men
and can be a barrier to finding help and understanding. We
need to create more awareness and understanding about the
extent of this problem in the male population. We need to
develop a safe environment for men to feel free about expressing
the way they feel.*

*Men with eating disorders are extremely sensitive and
emotional people and these two qualities are not sufficiently
recognised and accepted.*

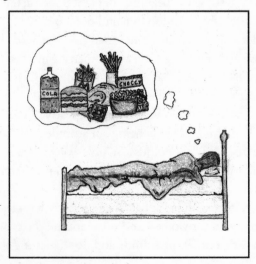

RISKS FOR MEN

Men have traditionally been left out of the beauty standards. We consequently assume that they do not suffer from dieting and eating disorders. I think this is a great misconception. As long as we keep saying that dieting distress is only a female issue, it will remain so.

According to the literature on eating disorders, males comprise about 10 per cent of all sufferers and they tend to be gay. We can take it for granted that heterosexual men will not readily admit to an eating disorder. They do not want to question their sexuality or suffer from what is viewed as a female issue. Nevertheless, men can suffer from an eating disorder just the same as women and in some cases the pressure is even greater. Because it is not recognised as being a man's problem, men suffer silently and in isolation. Men are supposed to be the great achievers, confident, and macho. Ironically, they are affected by appearance demands almost to the same extent as women are. Women can be thin and beautiful, or big and sexual; but the man has to be just right – not too thin and not too big.

Underweight men are at increased risk of steroid abuse and compulsive body-building. Overweight men are increasingly likely to diet just like women. 'Fat' for men has come to symbolise lack of self-control, laziness and even feminine softness.

The first step to recovery is to recognise the problem. We can all help in this area by changing our attitude to the male with an eating disorder. It is not just an 'only-women' trap. How the appearance obsession manifests itself in men is different, but it is still there.

Our culture with its 'appearance pressure' has created a lot of personal pain for women and men, and maybe now we will look at it with a different attitude and do something about it.

YOU ARE NOT ON YOUR OWN

Anon

At about fifteen years of age I noticed that food was playing a very important role in my life. I was constantly thinking, 'What am I going to eat next?' At first I did not mind. I quite enjoyed eating. I was tall and I could have done with a little extra weight. But as time went on these food thoughts were coming more and more to my mind. Sometimes I used to find that even after a substantial dinner I was still very hungry, and even if I felt physically full I could not stop. These feelings started to bother me. I was afraid that other people would notice that I was eating so much and I started to be embarrassed about my eating habits.

My eating became more and more secretive and slowly and surely it changed to binges. At that time I thought I was the only man on the whole planet who had this problem and that made things even worse. I was starting to panic. I did not know what was happening. I felt so desperate and lonely and the more I felt this way the less I wanted to see any other people. My friends slowly gave up on me and gradually I became a loner. My only company was my food. Now I can see, that each time I binged I forgot all my problems. I was numb, I did not feel, I did not think, I did not mark my existence. This went on for so long that I was afraid to look back and ask when it actually started. That would only bring more and more guilt, which I was full of anyway.

A time came when I knew I could not continue to go on this way, but I was not able to see any other way. I knew I had an eating disorder, but where was I to go from here? This is only a woman's problem. How could I have it? There must be something wrong with me. I went to numerous bookshops trying to find out more about it. But every book talked only of girls and women. I just felt I couldn't go on anymore, and I definitely couldn't tell anybody. What would they think? They'd probably lock me in a mental hospital. The despair was growing and I could not handle it anymore, so I decided to finish it forever. For a while I debated whether to do it, but then I knew I would feel like a failure who couldn't stick to anything. I did it.

Now ten years later I am so glad I did not succeed. I can't even remember everything that happened that night. Nobody ever talks about it in our house and I did not ask. It is better that way. My mum has since passed away and I am just sorry I could not explain things to her. But I am sure she is watching me somewhere and it was probably she who gave me the strength to go and fight this illness. It did take a long time. I was sent for treatment for depression and even there I could not tell them about my eating disorder. I just could not. But I learned more about myself and about life. Today I think I am nearly recovered. I am finishing my studies and I've found my own worth. I still cannot talk openly about my bulimia, but I have found somebody whom I trust and with whom I can be myself. I am being helped to let go of this monster. I know I am not the only man to suffer from this condition. There are thousands of us and knowing that helps a lot.

I just would like to say to all men who suffer as I did, please do something about it. You are not on your own. It is only people who have been there themselves who can bring about changes and re-educate our society about eating disorders. I hope the time will come when I can speak more openly about it. I do not wish anybody to feel the same way I used to.

A NOTE TO ALL YOU DOCTORS

Coleman

Some stories, if not all, have a beginning. A place we go to, where all that is present is put in context. A place where we develop an understanding of the now. These same stories do undoubtedly have a middle, a place which sets us up for the ending, the grand finale. A place which enables us to develop empathy, some more understanding and maybe, if we succeed, some compassion.

My fear in writing a story of this style is that, well, for one thing you may erroneously view me as a victim. A victim of family, life, circumstance. I want to assure you I am no victim. I fear that I may blame, and God knows I can blame. I spent a lot of years blaming. Today, however, it just does not seem appropriate. It doesn't even feel good anymore. I guess the main reason I want to start with the finish and end with the finish is that if I only present you with that, then maybe I won't get distracted and go all over the place and maybe I won't dramatise. This, however, I cannot guarantee, as drama has been one very large part of my eating disorder.

I don't want you to empathise with me, feel for me. I don't want you to know me. When I was in the middle of this tortuous disease some of you didn't want to know me. Some of you condescended with platitudes and told me to grow up or cop on. Some of you referred me on to yet another expert. Some of you exploited my fear. God knows, I allowed each of you to do as you saw fit. Each of you in your own way, I must believe, was trying to help me. Thankfully, even then, I was naïve enough to recognise that each of you had a price. With all of your dietary advice, medication, exercises and sessions, not one of you listened, not one of you heard what I was saying.

I am frightened and angry as I face hospitalisation yet again as a result of my eating disorder. It is not just the hospitalisation that has frightened me, it's all that has led up to it, it's all that has just happened. It's the questions I ask myself every morning when I wake and the fears I go to sleep with at night. I don't even trust myself anymore. Maybe I never did. Just yesterday I lied, yet again, to my best friend and supporter about pills I had taken. My shame, his pain. I don't want to hurt him anymore, I don't want to hurt me anymore.

Maybe it's true that there are two of us in this. Me and the disorder. The battle lines have been drawn. I know, for me, it's make or break this time. I am a 34-year-old man who suffers with an eating disorder. I am a sometime bulimic, a sometime anorexic, a sometime compulsive eater. I am an alltime shame and guilt man. There is a song in there somewhere, but some other day. I have been living with this eating disorder for most of my life. It has for the most part consumed my adult life. To the uninformed it may seem that this disorder would only affect a very small aspect of my life, that being food. This, however, could not be further from the truth. The disorder has affected and influenced every aspect of my life at one time or another.

Never did I make a decision without first consulting my eating disorder. It was he and only he who decided on what, where, who and when. He was powerful.

I strove for physical perfection. He told me I was still too fat! I strove for emotional fulfilment. He told me I wasn't worth it! I strove for mental stability. He told me I was crazy! I strove for all the things that you strive for and He told me I was not like you! He told me that you were better than me. I believed Him, and sometimes still do.

My body can't take much more. I'll find out the damage next week. My mind is confused and desperate for stability. Emotionally, I am raw and so god-awful vulnerable. I don't want to be the one to educate. I can barely keep my head above water as it is and you want me to tell you how to treat me!

It's hard to live in an average body when average won't do in a thin society.

9

STRANGE BUT TRUE

For those who have never suffered from an eating disorder and have never known the pain it causes, eating distress appears to be an enigma. It's very difficult to understand how people can harm themselves so much or why they might believe that they don't deserve to have the basic human need for food satisfied. There are many aspects of eating disorders that seem very strange and incomprehensible, but for those who experience them they are always real and genuine feelings.

In this chapter we try to show the real pain, fear and distress felt by those who suffer. We try to give an insight into their world through the words of those who have been there.

MIRROR, MIRROR
ON THE WALL.....

STRANGE BUT TRUE

Anon

For years people took me to be a confident, attractive, intelligent person, full of life, and very athletic. They complimented me on my great figure. What they didn't know was that I was also a great actress and that behind that smile lay a secret that hid mental torture and excruciating physical abuse. Strange but true! The mental torture was 'my secret', bulimia, which carried the weight of guilt, shame, fear, anxiety, depression, lies, isolation and low, low self-esteem. The physical abuse was an addictive fitness regime, hyperactivity, perfectionism, hours of eating and then vomiting which caused panic attacks, tension headaches, sleepless nights, blemished skin, rotten teeth – but it carried no extra body weight. I was in heaven when years ago I felt I needed to lose a 'bit' of weight to look better, be more confident, attract men etc., but when mixed with my screwed-up emotions these ingredients ended up being my diet of a nightmare in hell. Oh! those were bad days, unending, so secretive and full of darkness. A strange way to live, but for anybody with an eating disorder, so true.

Today, I am a recovering bulimic. I say this with a strange feeling of excitement and hope because for years I thought I was on my own and could not recover. Now I know this is not true. I have come through the nightmare and am living a life beyond my wildest dreams. Now I can open up to people, accept the disease and let the horribly guilty and shameful feelings fade away. I can relax and get on with living. It is not an easy road, but one that holds the possibility of learning and of changing every day. Even the bad days are good because something positive comes out of them. I live one day at a time.

As I write this I speak of my recovery which is full of hope. I have a 'disease' which I know will disappear, but only if I take action in simple steps on a daily basis. Like anyone with an illness my journey through recovery can be calm, it can be choppy or it can blow into a raging storm, but when I accept that the 'storms' are challenges necessary for change and growth, I go one step further to my destination. I am no longer the person I was. I believe in recovery – my own. When I look back (which I have to) on the last binge, last depression, the last year, I know I am moving forward. I keep my life simple by letting go the struggle and control. To do this I practise a spiritual, mental and physical programme. I live in the now.

Each day I ask God for help and guidance to get me through the 24 hours. There are days when I don't listen to him, but he is always there for me. I talk to myself a lot and tell myself how good I am, how good I look and how well I'm becoming. The gym, aerobic classes etc, are history and walking has become my primary 'well-being hobby'. I love it. It's easy, it's sociable and it gets me out and about. I don't push myself anymore. I'm getting older, wiser and well! If I feel stressed about money, I think back on the 'unmanageable' days where I didn't care about what I spent on 'junk and gorge' and realise that this 'stress' is a positive step towards my being more responsible and more aware of how I live. Living is not cheap!

Letting go of the 'eating' is one of the changes I find the hardest, but I take action. If I eat two digestive biscuits and the 'fat signal' starts buzzing in my head, I stop and picture 2 round flat buttons on the side of my hips and see that they look okay. (Before, my vision would have focused on 2 packets protruding from the hips, which is crazy.) When I 'feel' that I have eaten too much I look at others around me eating and see that they suddenly haven't changed into 'Mr. Blobbys'. They look the same as they did an hour earlier. I change into looser clothing to cope with the 'bloated tummy' or look in the mirror and see that it is 'normal'. When I get that 'tired after a meal sensation' I go with it and tell myself that this too shall pass – it does. If boredom sets in, I either take a long, relaxing bath, or pick up the phone. Speaking and sharing with someone else is the best way of getting out of my 'inner self'. I let go the me, me, me and focus my attention on those around me. Writing down my thoughts also helps me a lot.

I am at a stage in my recovery where every day, good or bad, I feel that life is good and that I am part of this goodness. But I keep asking myself, 'What do I really want from life?' This is causing me a bit of reflection, confusion and tension which if I was 'living a day at a time' and 'letting go the old' I shouldn't have. Obviously the fact that I am 'really feeling' and allowing myself to think of what I want from life is a big step in recovery. I am not shutting out my thoughts with food and body obsession.

I know what I don't want from life and that is the 'black hole' I have lived in for many years. I don't want the loneliness, secrecy, low self-esteem, self-abuse, self-destruction, depression, waste of time and secrecy and above all 'fear'. I was afraid to say no, afraid to say yes, afraid to hurt, afraid to love, afraid to grow out, afraid to grow big, afraid to 'grow up'. I was the child who wanted to be loved. I believed that the only way these wants could be fulfilled was by having a thin body. I am actually laughing right now as I type this, because I realise nobody really cares what shape my body is. It truly is the person inside the skin they care about. They love me and want me for who I am, flaws and all, and if they do worry about my body and how I look – well, that's their problem, not mine. It's great to be positive!

Expecting perfection from myself, fearing failure and reacting instead of acting, trapped my 'wants' for years. My choices were limited to what I expected of the reflection in the mirror and that wasn't much. I could never see what the reflection could give to others. When I finally made the choice to change and 'want recovery', the reflection changed. Its whole appearance became an ordinary human being and I could see myself as I really was. Changing and focusing on the 'hidden me' was hard and painful in the beginning but with the help of God, therapy and a support group I've learned now to cope with the new image, the new feelings, the growth, simply by taking slow, small steps one day at a time.

Looking back over the bleak periods of my life I cringe when I think of some of the things I did to attain the perfect image, but I can also laugh at them. Imagine jogging indoors for an hour and turning up the music so that nobody would hear; pretending I was having people coming to stay for a few days when shopping for a binge; or putting my empty wrappers in other bins so that nobody would find out about my secret. All crazy – strange but true.

I know that if I progress slowly but positively through this recovery, I will finally be able to answer the question, 'What do I really want from life?' Right now I want serenity and I know this can only be achieved by having hope and trust that all is well in my life.

THE NIGHTMARE

Mairéad

Imagine the terror, the horror of living with someone who
    was apt to physically and emotionally abuse you
    regularly.
Imagine the fear of not knowing where, when or how,
    but knowing the abuse would come eventually.
Now, just imagine the abuser was yourself.
That's what we food sufferers live with.

THE SIGN

Anon

I sat silently gazing out of my cosy warm room. The sky almost appeared to paint a picture, splashing reds and purples over what was an unspoilt scene. I remembered it so clearly. It reminded me of how I was feeling. I was deeply confused, but extremely emotionless.

I heard my mother's voice echo throughout the house as I threw some things together and headed for the door. Unusually, she decided to get a taxi. I sat in the back of the car, silently gazing out the window, fighting any thoughts that dared enter my mind. Then the driver began to talk. 'A lovely day,' he said. My mind was elsewhere. My mother made conversation. I heard him talk of his grandson and how he had been with him all that day. 'He is my pride and joy.' I smiled to myself as he continued about how he wasn't happy when he found out at first that his daughter was about to have Seán. This all changed when he saw him. He seemed the happiest man in the world, and all because of his grandson.

I sat back in the car. My eyes filled up. I thought how ironic the whole situation was. I was waiting for a sign and maybe it was a coincidence that I was 18, pregnant, and I was now going to England to arrange for a termination. I never wanted to go through with it but my parents were worried about my health because I had been suffering from an eating disorder for four years. I felt so guilty about all the pain I had put them through. If I had gone to England I would have put them through a lot more.

It is now one month later and I am not saying it is easy dealing with everything. I am frightened and that's okay. It's up to us to make the best of all the things that come our way. After all this I feel I am a stronger person. If it was the old me I really don't know what I would do.

A HUNGRY HEART

Anita

Everybody's got a hungry heart. Hungry for what?

Everyone is hungry for something different, but some people don't recognise it. They feed their hearts with food. They feed and numb the feelings, they numb the pain with food. These people don't feel physiological hunger, so they feed other hungers.

I don't feel physiologically hungry. I don't want food physically to keep me well and fit, but I need it and crave it. Just like I crave love and attention and, like many other people, when I don't get it, I eat.

When you deprive yourself of something that you really need, you will eventually take all you can and be unable to control it. This is what I do with food and when I can't handle what is good for me, I get rid of it. I run away from all that feels good. I push it away and dissociate myself from it and empty my life and my stomach.

At some stage this has to end. Someday you and I will have to accept some good and receive some love and some food in our lives. I hope, just like you do, that this day can come very soon and last forever. A life where we can accept everything we love and enjoy it in moderation.

DO YOU LOOK AT ME IN ENVY?

Anita

Do you look at me in envy?
Don't! I'm dying inside.
Do you look at me and think I'm fat?
It's none of your business anyway.
Do you look at me to condemn me for what I do?
Do you look at me like a circus animal?

Like a freak, with my gaunt face and deathlike skeleton.
Do you look at me and see disgust, like I do?
Do you look at me?
No, you're probably too busy loving me.

TRY TO SEE THE REAL ME

Nicola

I am writing this to you, because I want to show you, make you understand what it's like. Just a few minutes ago I sat down at the table with the family. They were eating a large dinner. Me? I was eating a small plain biscuit. I can't explain what it felt like to put that biscuit into my mouth. I could feel it. I could hear the crunch from it, but I could not taste a thing. When the biscuit went down my throat, I instantly felt guilty. 'My God, what have I done?' and almost automatically I could hear the voice in my head, 'You're going to be fat. That biscuit means you'll be heavier, uglier and fatter – all because you're greedy.'

People around me are trying to eat, and I am trying to be like them and saying to myself 'just a little', but I can't. The feeling of self-hatred, disgust and total remorse for what I've done is so unreal. It's like nothing I've ever known. It starts in your stomach and works its way slowly up through your throat until you can feel physically sick. I just hope and pray with all my heart and soul, you will never have to go through this.

Up until now, I've never had anyone who really understood what I was going through. But now I've got someone who cares enough to help me, who gives me the strength and courage to cope. I just want to say thanks to them all for helping me and believing in me and I really want to say how much I appreciate it and I really need it. I know I will get through one day.

When it is dark enough you see the stars.

Tuesday, 17 July 1979

Dear friend,

I'm back. Again you are the only one I can turn to. I have a lot to tell you. I am now becoming an expert at making my life a misery. The last few months have been hell. I hate myself, and everybody as well, my attitude ... and absolutely everything about me. The worst problem arising out of the whole sorry mess is that my money problem is back. I am stony broke, without a penny in my pocket.

Things got so bad that I could not even pay my rent. But I struggled through because I had to keep a roof over my head. The bingeing had got out of hand. It was taking all my extra cash. I got so bad and so low I even pawned my grandmother's rings. I had really hit rock bottom. I knew I could not ask my parents for any more hand-outs. My last resort was to get a part-time job as quickly as possible.

I started the next day. It was in a hotel on the other side of the city where no one knows me. I'm a washer-up in the kitchens. It is horrible, dirty and smelly. The waitresses and waiters just throw the dishes at me. 'Wash this, Marie; do this, Marie.' Very seldom do I hear the word 'please'. It is hard going. I feel humiliated and depressed. I want to eat all the time, but rarely have enough for food. I have to pay off my debts. But the biggest problem is that I am a pig. Yes, a pig. When nobody is looking I eat the left-overs from the customers' plates. Writing to you now I am crying. I cannot stop. I am so full of sadness. Yes, I know I am feeling sorry for myself but just look at the way things have worked out for me. Nothing has gone right. All I have left now is to cry.

If only things could be different. But I know that is not reality. I have no work today. It is my day off. I have nothing to do. Tomorrow I will be back at my work and again eating the left-overs from the plates. I will stuff all the scraps into my stomach, which I hate so much. The chef offers me my meals, because all the staff are entitled to their meals. But I always refuse saying I have eaten earlier. You see, I find it hard to actually throw out the scraps. I do not know why. I envy the customers who pay for the lovely meal and do not eat it. I envy them for having the money in the first place to allow them to come to such a expensive hotel to eat and then to leave some behind.

I hate myself. I disgust myself. What would my parents say if they knew what I am doing? It does not bear thinking about. I know I cannot stop, no matter how hard I try. Something goes click! It happens in a split second. A strange power comes over me. I am then another person and I am out of control. I sometimes do not know what I am doing. For a time I feel good. Nothing touches me or can harm me. I feel as if I am in a dark tunnel, no worries, no hurt. It is like a drug, but as with drugs the feeling soon wears off and the craving gets worse. I ask myself, how do 'normal' people manage to eat just a little and manage to stop, eat one biscuit and stop. They do not want more. They are satisfied. With me it is the opposite. The more I eat the more I want and the hungrier I feel.

If I stop to think of what germs or disease I could get from this it turns my stomach and my soul. Yet I cannot stop. I am like an animal. I am a dreadful person. I look awful. My eyes are puffy and red from lack of sleep. My face is swollen. I have no energy now, not even for living. What will become of me?

Marie

Monday, 8 October 1979

My friend,

Still I am confused. I do not know who I am. You recognise your old friend the whinger is back. One day I am down and feeling low and depressed and I almost enjoy my isolation and confusion. The next day I am on the top of the world, making big plans, bigger than I would ever be able to cope with. Then almost immediately the smallest problem can throw me. I cannot find a happy medium. It is all or nothing. Then my salvation is the coffee shop and the food stores and all they have to offer. I think at times I am going insane. I must be mad. This kind of carry-on cannot be normal. Maybe I am ready for the men in the white coats.

You know my old slimming habit. You know what I am talking about. I have lost a couple of pounds in weight. I needed to after all the weight I piled on. I am five foot five, and weigh eight and half stone. But every time I put some food in my mouth I feel like fifteen stone. The worst is trying to overcome this feeling and it gets so bad that in the end I just stuff myself more. I just cannot stop it. The funniest thing is that I can go without food for several days, managing only coffee and natural yoghurt. But the instant I eat something the urge is back and stronger than before and I am out of control and cannot stop. All my willpower goes. All the resolutions fly out the window, all my plans evaporate into thin air.

I know if I had a boyfriend my eating problem would be solved. I would be quite well. I am very lonely. I miss somebody. I need somebody to care for me, to like me, to be there for me. I know I will never find anyone. Who would want me? The only way I can forget this loneliness is when I am eating. But my old habit of getting rid of the food is back haunting me. The fear of getting fat is as great as it was before and I have to get rid of the food. There is nothing I can do about that. And after I get rid of the food the depression sets in these days a hundred times worse than before. It is a vicious circle and there does not seem to be any end to it.

I am feeling physically wrecked. I have aches and pains all over my body. Everything hurts, muscles, joints, bones. My nails are breaking, my hair is falling out, my skin is very coarse and dry. I look like a shrivelled old witch. I have not been able to manage to solve my financial problems. I am still broke. I am working all the hours I can with nothing to show for them. That too is killing me.

I'm twenty-four years old with nothing. To think it could have been so different. I could be a doctor by now. I had so many plans and hopes for myself for the future. Yet here I am, living in a dingy flat. I work as a receptionist part-time in one hotel, and I wash dishes at night in another hotel. I am a total food junkie. Yes, that is what it has come to. Doesn't it sound terrible?

My conscience is driving me mad. I did something terrible. I cannot even begin to understand why I did what I did. I hate to say this but I am a thief. I know I have really overstepped this time. You see, I did not have enough money to pay my rent and it was overdue. The landlord was calling all the time and I was afraid of losing my flat. I was desperate. The answer to my problems came in the form of two gentlemen who booked in late to the hotel where I am a receptionist. I was on shift work, and it was quite late. The gentlemen paid in cash and as they were very tired they went straight to their rooms, booking an early call. I was left at the desk with their cash in my hand. I suddenly felt that this money was the answer to my prayers. The idea would not go away and kept pestering me. I was still holding the money. I had not put it into the register. What would happen if I did not register the money or record the men in the book? Would I get away with it? Would it be missed? My need at this moment was greater than the consequences. I simply pocketed the money and did not need any more persuasion.

The rest of the evening was uneventful. What I had done kept flashing back to my mind. I made millions of excuses. I would make up to my employers and work harder for them in the future. For a little while that idea seemed to rid me of the feelings of guilt. But the little voice in my head was telling me that I needed this anguish because I was such a terrible person. I needed this guilt.

Marie

Tuesday, 9 October 1979

Dear friend,

Something terrible has happened. My boss has found out. He called me into his office. 'Marie, we seem to have a problem and we are hoping you can throw some light on it for us.'

He proceeded to tell me about the two gentlemen. They had booked in for one night, then because of business commitments decided to stay on another night. 'They claim they paid in full for one night, Marie,' said my boss, 'yet we do not appear to have any record of them in the register. They assure me they paid in cash and so we have no proof of it.'

I knew what was coming next but at this moment I wanted the ground to open up and swallow me. I was caught this time with my hand literally in the till.

'Well, Marie, what have you to say?'

I could not speak. My throat was dry, my hands were sweating and my whole body was shaking. My face went red. I was sure he could see that I was definitely guilty by the state I was in.

He was now staring hard at me, still talking, but I could no longer hear what he was saying. My head was spinning and I felt dizzy. I could not stop what happened next. I started to cry and blurted out: 'I did it. I took the money. I'm sorry. I'll pay it back. I'm sorry.'

There was silence for a moment. Everything seemed to stop.

My boss spoke quietly. 'I'm sorry, Marie, and I am also very disappointed. I know that this sort of thing can happen in hotels, but not in a million years would I ever have thought that it would be you. You do know what the consequences will be? We will have to terminate your contract and unfortunately I will have to inform your other employer.'

I was hysterical by this stage. I did not even know what I was talking about only that I was begging him for another chance. I begged him to spare me. I told him I really needed my job. And I assured him that I would pay back the money. He thought for a while. Finally he said, 'Marie, I do not want to destroy your future. I do hope you have learned a hard lesson. I will give you a chance. I will not contact your other employer. What happened here is between the two of us and we will keep it that way. Remember, Marie, not everyone will be as merciful as I am. Your future is in your own hands.'

I am desolate.

Marie

Saturday, 20 October 1979

Dear friend,

I have now pawned all the rest of the jewellery I ever had, including stuff my grandmother and mother gave me. All the money I ever got for it has gone on binges. I would start out with good intentions about what I was going to do with the money, put it towards the rent and pay off my debts, but it always ended up feeding my habit. I cannot explain it. I have no logical reason for anything anymore. Nobody will understand, not even myself.

Now I have nothing left to sell, no gold, no clothes. I have resorted to buying second-hand clothes and now my night job is gone. I could not even manage to hold onto a washing-up job. The only think I have left now is my body. One evening shortly after the terrible event in the hotel, I was out, walking aimlessly. Suddenly I realised I was on Green Square, a famous place for picking up girls. I watched for a while. The girls were scantily dressed and strutted their wares along the pavements for all to see. Some looked young and some more mature, some looked intelligent, some looked like real bimbos. Yet I envied them all. I would love to be able to do what they're doing, to stand there like they do and sell themselves. I bet none of them has any money worries. Why can I not sell my body? I don't even like it. It is torturing me. I hate sex, but I am sure I could satisfy a man. I know what they are like and what they expect. It would not take long. I know they would have to touch me but at the end of it I would be paid. I wondered how much the girls were paid for their services. I would love to talk to one of them and ask them what it is like, but I am sure they would not entertain the likes of me. They might get angry with me and think that I was trying for their business.

I began to walk slowly away and suddenly a car pulled up beside me. A man rolled down the window. I was scared, yet curious. I did not know what to say.

'Hello, little one, are you looking for some company?'

A bald head appeared out of the window. A man old enough to be my father, no, my grandfather, peered at me through the darkness. His look was almost undressing me right there. Instantly I forgot myself. I was so angry the blood began to rush to my brain. The fury inside me was so strong I felt I could push his stupid car off the road.

'F.... off, you filthy pig,' I shouted, then I ran.

I did not stop running until I had got off the square, then I looked back to see if he was still there. There was nothing only the darkness. Thank God the bus arrived then. I jumped on and collapsed on to a seat. I was so relieved to be safely on the bus and away from that awful place. What in the name of God was I thinking about? I still have my money problems but right now I no longer envy those poor unfortunate girls. In a strange way I admire them. I honestly could not do what they do. But I am sure they have their own reasons.

Marie

'Things do not change. We change.' Henry D. Thoreau

10

IT'S NEVER TOO LATE

It's never too late to change. If you find you are unhappy in a situation you can change that. Some people with eating disorders are told that there is no cure, that they will simply have to cope with it. That, of course is not true. Anyone can recover from an eating disorder. No one has to live with it. Recovery is possible for everyone. It's never too late. If you can imagine life without an eating disorder then you can live without an eating disorder. If you can't quite imagine it yet, don't worry. Read these testaments of the many people who've recovered and let your imagination run riot.

IT'S NEVER TOO LATE

Helen

Give up now.
What's the point?
It never ends.
So why not lead your hand again to these binges
That make your life so complete.
Complete – did I hear you say?
Are you mad?
What about today
And the life ahead
Where time is standing still
Waiting for you to avail of it
And get out of this rot?
Where ever you are, child,
Don't let it hide.
That person inside has so much to give
So much hope ...
What ever happens ... let yourself live.
It's never too late.

LIFE

Anon

'She has two weeks to live ... She will not survive ... She has to eat
or she will die ... There is nothing you can do ... She needs to try
harder ... She needs to put more effort into it ...' These are the
words which my mother had to listen to constantly, everywhere
she sent me. I felt so guilty that I really wanted to die. I could not
put my parents through any more. I knew I had no power to get
better, and I had little will to live. To be honest I did not even
want to get better because getting better meant putting on

weight. I just could not see myself as 8 stone. I would just not be able to handle it. I was so confused, tired, fed up, sick, I just could not see the point of living here in this world.

Everybody watched me. Every time I put something in my mouth my parents nearly celebrated. All the while I was thinking, How will I get rid of it? Where will I exercise? Each time I went to the doctor I was weighed like cattle for the market. I found it so humiliating. It was like I did not have any qualities other than my weight. How could a few extra pounds make me a good person? It was a nightmare but thank God I survived – all the suicide attempts and I survived them all.

For somebody who has never experienced something similar it must be hard to understand, but the truth is that each time I did it and survived I realised that I had to live and carry on. Strange as it may sound it built me up and I am a stronger person for it. When you hear nothing but death threats and blackmail you begin to want it, not only for yourself but also for the sake of the people who love you. So many times I went to bed at night wishing I would not wake up and that my parents would be free to live their own lives again. I often wondered why they cared for someone as awful as me and why they did not just let me go. Why was I so bad, so difficult? Why was I born? Why was I alive? I felt so guilty – guilty for living, guilty for breathing, guilty for being bad, for being who I was.

Today three years later I see the matter differently, and believe it or not I am glad I am here. Eventually I found somebody who understood and helped me to find the reasons for living. And I would like to thank my parents, and all the people who cared for me through the illness, for being there and never giving up on me. Life did change for the better, and it is a miracle but I am nearly nine stone and I do actually feel really good about myself. I am back at work, learning to enjoy ordinary activities, which I deprived myself of for so long.

Even though I consider myself nearly recovered I know I still have some work to do on my self-development. But the most important thing is that I am enjoying the whole process of recovery. I take it day by day, knowing that after surviving all I went through, nothing can happen that I wouldn't be able to handle. It is so challenging to discover that you have good qualities as well, that people can like you for the person you are and that you can eat, without constantly thinking that every mouthful is going to ruin your life, without constantly reminding yourself that you are not good enough and that only by losing an extra pound can you make up for it. It is a wonderful feeling of freedom to be able to concentrate on the taste of the food and forget to count the calories, to be actually able to read the menu without a panic attack.

For a number of reasons I still cannot sign this, but maybe one day ... But I would love to tell people who know somebody who is going through a similar situation: please, do not frighten them with death. Please do not give out to them for being the way they are. They feel bad enough about themselves without being reminded. Love them for what they are. Be there for them when they ask for your help. This is the only way you can help them to get out of this misery.

FOR YOU ALL

Anita

Please don't punish yourself any more
You are strong and important.
I know this. If you could only see it.
I would not destroy, or cause you a moment's pain.
I see no reason for that. You don't deserve it.
Please see what I see.

My eyes see the whole picture,
Which is different from what you think I see.
I see you sick, I see you in pain, I see you sad,
I see you hurting yourself when there is no need.
All I want to do is help.
I also see your beauty. I see you strong. I look up to you,
And my respect grows with every hardship you get
    through.
Please keep on fighting with all the strength you have,
Not because I ask you to,
But so that one day
You can share with my eyes and see the wonder in you
    that I do.

THE HIDDEN NIGHTMARE

Nicola

I suppose on the outside I look like one of those fortunate
people, who has everything going for them – an outgoing,
friendly person with a loving family and a kind, attentive
boyfriend. I have no reason to be unhappy, except for always
having to keep my distance from people, in case they discover my
awful secret. Deep down I really hate myself such a lot and feel
unworthy of anyone's love or attention. For four years I lived in
mortal fear that this disgusting habit of mine would be
discovered. Life became a game of cat and mouse. My boyfriend
and family wondered why I spent so long in the bathroom,
supposedly washing my hair and so on. I turned a blind eye to
the fact that there was something wrong. I can't put into words
how painful it felt waking up and realising I was in one hell of a
mess.

At times I know I am nearly slim, but never slim enough.
The proportions of my body will never be right. Never a day goes

by when I don't look in the mirror and look at the ugly rolls of flesh hanging from all over my body. My face is too round, my stomach too fat and so on. Sometimes I think the only thing that would make me happy would be a total body transplant.

I dread the thought of ever becoming fat, because I think I would lose respect. People would treat me with contempt and see that I have no control. My size would be proof of my muddled, greedy, pathetic, self-indulgent nature.

No one can stand being near me for long. One moment I'm lively and loving, the next I become this desperate person, self-centred and mean. Sometimes I feel I am living a double life. I'm a complete workaholic and want everything to be right. I'll spend days thinking about what a failure I am and wonder what is the point in trying. Each day is a variation on the same theme: eating, guilt, vomiting ... All the time, effort and energy I spend on my obsession is driving me to the brink of total despair.

For years I was sent from specialist to specialist and kept getting the same lecture. None of them understood how I felt. They didn't know the guilt I had to deal with after I'd eaten a slice of toast or an apple. So many times life seemed to be so pointless, but even writing this, deep down I know I am going to overcome my eating disorder. Now I am getting help from someone who understands and cares and I am learning to believe it. It is hard, but I know I will live my life one day. I will live free!

SOMEDAY

Mairéad

I feel so guilty for eating, for wanting to eat,
 for making myself sick, for being so fat and ugly
 ... and not doing enough about it.
I wish all these horrible feelings

would just go away and leave me in peace.
I hate feeling like this, feeling so useless and empty,
    feeling like it'll never end, never go away
    and I'll never be free ...
But I have to believe, I have to believe in me.
I don't believe in myself very much at the moment,
    but some day I will.
Some day I'll be free and then I can let the people who
    care and worry about me be free too.
I've chained myself and only I have the key to my
    freedom.
I just have to figure out how to unlock the chains and
    throw them aside.
Someday nothing will bind me, not food, calories, fat,
    weighing scales
    or the wistful 'why can't I look like that?'
How will I know that day has come?
I'll wake up, I'll be me ...
    and, that will be good enough.

FEELING DEPRESSED?

Karen

How often do you feel it is too late, that there is no point in
continuing? Here is a recipe which will help you.

INGREDIENTS
  1 body and soul
  1 conscience
  1 walkman
  2 legs
  1 sea

NUTRITIONAL INFORMATION
  1 exercise
  2 oxygen
  3 sense of well-being and
    satisfaction

METHOD
1. Retain the body and soul.
2. Weigh out conscience and mix it well with your thoughts. Try to realise that this is your life and that no-one or nothing is going to take your happiness away from you. This is a transitional period in your life, when you don't know whether you are here for a purpose or just to amuse your fellow companions.
3. Finally, take your lovely and beautiful legs, mix well with the walkman and carry yourself off down to the magical and mysterious seafront. Let the sea cast a spell over this thing which people call depression or eating distress.

RESULT

By now you may feel at ease with your body and soul. Take note of how this feels and try to confront your misleading thoughts.

The depression has now evaporated and you watch it rise up into the atmosphere to join all the other lonely, puffy clouds high up in the big, bright blue, far out of harm's reach.

Achieving starts with believing.

Tuesday, 6 July 1982

Hello again, my friend,

Just to keep you updated on events and to let you know that I am still around. Usually I only write to you when I am in bad form. I am trying very hard to keep everything in place and keep myself in line but that is very difficult and I still lapse back into my old habits. Happily that is not the case today. I want to share some good times with you.

Great news! I finally found a man - and he actually liked me! I am married now and pregnant. The pregnancy has changed me a lot. I am on top of the world, and I am very surprised at the way I am feeling. This Marie who is usually so hyper, or else completely down and unhappy, has somehow let go of the past. I find it amazing and hard to believe that I am so tranquil in myself.

My relationship with John has not improved. He has not accepted my pregnancy. We have never spoken much about it. We continue to lead separate lives. I am just concentrating on the baby, though deep down I have not given up completely and am hoping that when the baby arrives he might change. That hope is keeping me going now. I am enjoying being pregnant. I feel happy. I often laugh when I can feel it moving around inside me. It is a wonderful feeling. I have someone to live for, someone who will need me. All my thoughts are preoccupied with the arrival now of the baby. Often I wonder will it be a boy or a girl, though that does not matter at all. I wonder who it will look like. I am so excited I can hardly wait. I'm trying not to think too much about the labour.

I have heard so many horror stories. I am sure the physical pain will not bother me. I am never afraid of pain. Oh, I nearly forgot what I wanted to tell you. As you can imagine I buy everything I can get my hands on about new babies. I came across a most interesting article in one of the magazines. According to the article I am actually suffering from a mental disorder. Imagine ME suffering from an mental illness! The story in the magazine describes a women who has done exactly the same as I have done over the years, the overeating, starving, bingeing, laxatives, constantly exercising, you name it ....

She always felt bad about herself, suffered from depression, worried about putting on weight, even though she only weighed eight stone. I have to say it was marvellous to discover that I was not alone, that there were others like me. For so long I had felt that I was the only one who suffered like this. Now I was finding out there were others who behaved as madly as I did. But it was being recognised as a mental illness. The psychiatrists have named it 'bulimia'.

What an ugly name! Could they not come up with a better one? The name alone gave me the shivers. I did not like even saying it. But I was very interested in the article and read it over and over. It was the first time I had ever heard or read anything about it. But sadly it did not give any phone number or address of the person who wrote it. I would like desperately to talk to that person. Yet it did me good to identify with someone else in the same position. I laughed to think that I was being linked to mental illness. Looking in the mirror, I kept pointing and calling myself a 'crazy woman'. I know I have been crazy in the past, but honestly I would not go so far as to say I was mentally ill. No, that was unthinkable, not acceptable. But thank God it will be in the past one day.

That was something definite that came out of the pregnancy. During the early days I failed a couple of times, actually a good few times when I got really low. But that was when the trouble with John was at its peak. Now things are better. I can eat what I like, keep it down, and not have to worry about the way I look.

I know I have to eat healthily and look after the baby. This is the most important part of my life. I feel I have conquered my food problem. I don't like looking back into the past, because of what I will see and remember.

I am starting anew and I am determined to be a new Marie.

Marie

Sunday, 19 December 1982

Dear friend,

Still the only friend I have. Probably the only one I will ever have. Life, as you can imagine, has been hectic. I did not have time to write to you.

Yes, I survived the pregnancy and the birth. I have a lovely baby girl, Jane. She is adorable. I love her to bits. I cannot take my eyes off her. I'm finding it hard to believe she is actually mine. It is wonderful to have someone. I am still getting used to the idea. It is all very exciting.

The pregnancy seemed very long. There were times I thought the baby would never be born and I was so worried and full of guilt for what I did in the past. Near the end was the hardest. I was admitted to the hospital and had to lie up for nearly the last four weeks before she was born. That was good at the end because the atmosphere at home was still bad and I was delighted to leave it behind for a while. John and I were still leading separate lives, and there did not seem to be any signs of a reconciliation. John is hardly ever at home and I wonder how foolish I was believing it would change after the baby was born. It was very sad in hospital having nobody to visit me. When Jane was born he was not waiting expectantly and nervously like the other fathers and there was no great welcome for her or no apology or 'let's start all over again' for me. In fact, quite the opposite. He saw her, yes, but just for a second. That was it, nothing more. He had to go. He was too busy. I could not understand it. How could he be so cold? There was no explanation, just a big nothing. I was hurt to the core.

Jane cried a lot, which is natural. He could not handle that at all and would get annoyed and complain about it constantly. His way of coping with her was usually to leave. That suited us fine. It is easier with him gone. Less to worry about. Jane, I will have to admit, did cry more than any other baby I knew, but I was informed by the nurse and the hospital that this happens sometimes and that it will pass.

I was very worried about her and found it hard to sleep. The old nightmares would come flooding back and begin to haunt me. I was feeling more guilt on top of the guilt I had already. It was weighing me down. Not only had I damaged my own health, I had probably damaged this unfortunate child as well, and, worse, put her in danger too. Oh God, please help me! I am so low. I am now praying day and night. I will make it up to God and to Jane. I will try harder. It is all getting on top of me. I am trying to make the best of it. What else can I do? I am on my own and unfortunately the old problem is raising its ugly head again and this time I am failing miserably. My willpower is letting me down and since having Jane I am hungrier than ever before, and now all the time.

Eating is the only way I can relax. I look terrible. I have put on so much weight. I am like a balloon. Nothing fits me. All my clothes are too small. I look as if I never had the baby at all. So much for my dream of being a lovely slim mum pushing her beautiful baby around for everyone to see. The reality again is the opposite except that Jane is beautiful. I hope she is not ashamed of having such a horrible mother. I do not blame John for not wanting me anymore, but I cannot understand why he turned against his child, who has done nothing. It is all my fault, I know it. But I want to make her life easier and happier than mine is. I am determined to do that for her. I have not got all the answers, and even sitting writing to you trying to make some sense of it all, I really want to put down the pen and run to the kitchen and stuff my face. Where is this going to end?

Marie

Wednesday, 12 January 1983

My friend,

Where do I begin? I am sitting here alone in my bed trying to make some sense of what has happened and why it happened. It is slowly beginning to dawn on me what I did and why. I need to talk to you more than ever before. My mind is racing. I'm baffled as to why I let it happen.

It all happened two days ago. It was nearly four in the morning. Everyone was asleep, except me. I just do not know what came over me. I guess I'll never know. I lost my pride, my dignity, everything. No, I did not lose it. I gave it away. How could I have been so silly. Such an idiot!

With John I have nothing in common anymore. This is nothing new. I just find it hard to believe, nevertheless. The sex side of our marriage was gone. Actually it was never there, but that didn't bother me. We rarely talked except to argue. But this evening John came home earlier than usual, and stayed in for the night, which was unusual. For a long time I was assuring myself that I did not need him, I had Jane. But somehow that night I just could not sleep. I knew I should try and make it up with John, hoping he would change and things would be fine again. I do not know where I got the courage from. Without too much thought I decided on action. I went to his bedroom. I was nervous. I was afraid of rejection but my need was too great now. This was my last chance. John was snoring and I could smell alcohol from his breath. I crept into his bed and gently rubbed his head. I just kept looking at him and wondering where we had gone wrong. I wanted to apologise for being me. He opened his eyes. With a look of surprise on his face he managed to stammer, 'What are you doing, Marie?' 'Just lying beside you and looking at you. Is it a crime for a wife to want to look at her husband?' I asked. I hardly got the sentence finished when he sat upright in the bed and pushed me aside. 'Are you crazy? I'm tired. Go back to bed.'

'John,' I pleaded. 'I need to talk to you. We can be a family again ...' I spluttered out. I surprised myself, and surprised him even more because he shot straight up in the bed and shouted, 'Just look at yourself. You are an ugly, fat, depressed, sad woman. You do not attract me anymore. Even your night-dress is too small for you. What we had is gone. I do not love you anymore. It's finished. I have had enough. Do I have to spell it out for you? It is over. All we can do is remain under the same roof and get on with our lives as best we can. I am an unhappy man. You depress me even more. I think Jane would be better off with my mother before you ruin her life too ....'

John had hardly finished his speech when I started to cry uncontrollably. His words were ringing in my ears. I was heartbroken. What he had said was just too hard to handle, for anybody. I left the room.

I went downstairs. First I checked on Jane. Thank God she was sleeping soundly. I searched for a drink. Anything would do. I just needed something. I found a bottle of whiskey. I saw my salvation, my road to oblivion. I did not even bother looking for a glass. I opened the bottle and drank and drank to drown the pain. I smoked cigarette after cigarette, all the time repeating to myself, 'You are a fat, ugly, bad mother. Everything and everybody would be better off if you did not exist ...' Yes, I am no good to anyone. I have destroyed John's life. I might do the same to Jane. I can't take that chance. I have let everyone down, especially my parents. All the hurt I have caused them over the years. And I can't stop doing what I am doing. I keep on doing it. I am so ashamed. All the hope I ever had is gone now. Now at least I know the reason for John's behaviour. I am not what he wants me to be. He is ashamed of me.

I went to the bathroom where I hide sleeping tablets. I used to collect them just in case ... I remember the doctor telling me they were quite strong - that is what I needed to know. All that was registering in my head at that moment was that I was no use to anyone, not even myself. I was unwanted and unloved.

I poured some water. I took all the sleeping tablets, and swallowed them down with water and what was left of the whiskey. I tried not to think, but just prayed. I prayed, 'Oh God, forgive me. Please help my parents understand. Do not let them be angry with me. Look after John and Jane. I love them both. I know they will all be better off without me. I will not complicate their lives anymore. I am sorry for all my mistakes. Oh God, forgive me ...'

I began to feel sleep coming on me and for a while I thought I was in heaven. Through a cloudy haze I could see myself as a little girl. I was with my parents playing in a field, which was filled with bluebells and poppies. I was so happy. My mother picked some flowers, made a garland and put them around my head. She was laughing and happy. She was hugging and kissing me. She looked so young and happy. Then my father appeared to take me to school. He too was happy. Then I saw my university days. John arrived, telling me how much he loved me and I could see the details of our wedding. It was strange. It was as if it was all happening again. I cannot explain it, though it all seemed very real. It was paradise, where there was no sadness. All I could feel was a great sense of love and acceptance and of being special. I was really happy here. I wanted to stay.

But I woke up and when I did I was surprised to find myself in John's bed, feeling dreadful. My head and my stomach were both hurting, one worse than the other. I was dizzy and so weak I could hardly get out of the bed. Anyway, I really did not want to. What had happened? I had obviously failed in my attempt. Slowly it began to dawn on me. First the row with John crept back into my mind, the cruel words, the hurt and the pain and the emptiness. I could remember leaving his room. Why was I now back in his bed ? Digging deeper into my mind the confusion began to clear and the awful realisation began to hit me. It really scared the living daylights out of me. I had come so near. How did I survive it all? But, oh God, was I glad that I had failed in my attempt. My desire to live was suddenly very strong. The more I realised what I had done the more I was determined to live and to make the best of it. How could I do this to Jane? Where is the sensible Marie? How could I allow this to go so far? I knew now it was up to me to get out of this mess.

Once again I was going to start all over. Even though I was feeling weak and dizzy I felt strong in my mind. I sat upright in the bed. I could not hear Jane. Where was she? Somehow I managed to relax. I felt she was okay. I needed this time to. I needed to think things out. I was going to prove to myself and to Jane that I would be the best mother in the world.

I was beginning to realise that John was the cause of my depression and I decided that he was not worth it. I had been trying all the time to have a father for Jane, and in the process she nearly lost her mother. This thought frightened me. I did not feel hate toward John. I felt he was out of my system. There was no hate, no love. Right now I wanted to see my daughter and hug her and kiss her forever. The door opened and there stood John with Jane in his arms. This was an unusual sight. He rarely had any time for her. Jane looked at me. I stretched my arms to her. It was good to feel her. She was so warm and comforting. I was glad I was alive. I realised that life was the most precious gift that we shall ever receive. Life comes free and sometimes what is free is not appreciated. I had nearly lost it. Now I promised Jane that I was going to learn to value it!

Marie

The only person you can control is yourself.

11

RECOVERY

In this section we offer you a few suggestions which helped other people in recovering from eating disorders. It is a well-known fact that people learn from each other and if something helped one person, maybe it can be of help to somebody else; it may be of help to you.

RECOVERY

Recovery means something different to every person. But in our experience in the clinic where I work, we find that nearly everybody's recovery includes the points listed below. Examine these and rate yourself on a scale from 1 to 10. Then you can assess how far you have got and to what areas you need to pay further attention.

1. Gaining freedom from food obsession
2. Gaining freedom from body obsession
3. Learning to know yourself
4. Learning to be aware of yourself
5. Learning to accept yourself
6. Learning to believe in yourself
7. Emphasising honesty
8. Living in the present
9. Taking care of your physical health
10. Being open to forming new relationships
11. Giving to others and learning to receive
12. Being able to talk about your real feelings
13. Having clarity of thought
14. Increasing spirituality
15. Gaining the ability to have real fun in life
16. Loving yourself the way you are

All things must be accomplished mentally before they are accomplished physically. So you need to believe you will recover; you need to visualise yourself free before you can actually become free. Here are some pointers as you move in that direction:

◊ Concentrate on your successes, not failures. Recovery is like snakes and ladders. Failures do not really exist if you take them as learning opportunities. The important thing is to make overall progress.

◊ Loneliness is not cured by human company. Loneliness is cured by contact with reality.

◊ Learn about how the body really works. Allow yourself to know your body. Get in touch with your body. Pay attention to at least one body sensation that you experience each day, to help you begin to identify feelings, tension spots, tingling, hot or cold feeling, pain. Pay attention to negative body talk. Begin by stopping yourself and then work towards making positive statements. Do this at your own pace.

◊ Look at photos of admirable people whose bodies are not in the cultural idealised image. Focus on what qualities you admire in them, rather than judging their worth on appearance. Admirable people come in various sizes and shapes.

◊ The only way to keep slim is to eat, breathe, move. Eating smaller portions but more often, prevents bloating and allows you to get used to having food inside. Choose food that you enjoy and is comforting. Allow yourself to taste it. Eat regularly, even mechanically, until you develop body signals. If you are bingeing ask yourself:

> What does it give to me?
> Does it relax me?
> Does it numb me?
> Can I get the same result any other way?
> Do I have other choices?
> Do I deserve more?

◊ Make mealtime a pleasant occasion. Eating on the run builds up guilt and stress and we lose touch with what we have eaten. This can bring panic. Try to eat at regular times and always while sitting down. Wear comfortable clothes, made from soft materials. If you have vomited, eat something nourishing to prevent the cycle continuing. If you get sick, put some toothpaste on your gums; do not brush your teeth. Be aware of trigger situations which contribute to overeating. Write them down. Always be prepared to start again. The golden rule is: never give up.

◊ Talk to people and develop curiosity about people. Allow

yourself to be real rather than dreaming about an ideal. Let go of words like should, ought, must. Live in grey instead of 'black and white'. Feel proud of each achievement, however small.

◊ Take your place in the universe. Keep your diary about positive feelings. It will have an effect on your immune system. Feeling good builds up your immune system. Our natural painkillers, endorphins and enkephalins, are ten times stronger than morphine.

◊ The more you put into recovery the more you get out of it. You need to get better for yourself, not for anybody else. Learn to understand who you are. You might discover that you are a very interesting and special person. Express your opinions. The more you express, the less you need to suppress.

◊ If you feel a binge coming on, apply delaying tactics:

  • Phone someone or put on some nice music and dance to it.
  • Knit, or go for a walk, or take a shower.
  • Make a list of foods you are going to binge on, seal it and throw it out.
  • Repeat to yourself, 'It will pass ... it will pass ... '
  • Count how much a binge can cost, and what other things you could buy with that money.
  • Picture yourself in the bathroom throwing up after a binge. Be realistic – red eyes, swollen face, bloated feeling, depression, guilt ... Ask yourself, 'Is that what I really want?'
  • Remind yourself endlessly, 'I deserve more, I deserve more, even if I do not believe it yet.'

◊ Try to see yourself in perspective. Remind yourself that you have the power to master your feelings and the power to succeed. Every minute you feel good about yourself is an investment in the future. Instead of analysing what did happen and why, ask yourself what you can do about it.

In the following pages we suggest 31 tips, which can help sufferers of eating disorders. Try one a day.

ACTION DAYS

DAY 1   *Count the achievements*

Today remind yourself that it is not only knowledge that counts but the action as well. Recovery from a food problem calls for knowledge of how to do it, but it also involves being willing to do it. Let today be a day of action. Decide on something you would like to change, just something small for a start. It is better to succeed gradually in small achievements – they can prevent big disappointments. Every metre is made from centimetres. Every day we do something right, but we usually ignore these small achievements. How often do you give yourself credit when it's due? Start right now. Credit yourself for every small thing you do right from this moment, even just for opening this book. You might be bingeing or starving, but instead you are reading about recovery. Credit yourself for it.

For the rest of the day pretend you are a detective who is looking for everything that you did well. A detective uses a magnifying glass. You can use one too. Look carefully. Every small achievement counts. Only small things build up a big case. Recovery is built up from thousands of small changes and achievements every day. Write them down and go over them as much as possible.

Every action brings a result. If you do not like the result, change the action.

DAY 2   *Be kind to yourself*

This whole book is about you and for you. You would not have an eating disorder if you were thinking about yourself in a more positive way and believing in your good points. Often we who suffer from this condition are called 'very selfish'. We are not selfish, but we can be so self-centred and wrapped up in our negativity that our behaviour can come across as being selfish. Most of us know only the negative things about ourselves, and we often remind ourselves of these. The eating disorder is our comfort. After so much negativity we do need the comfort.

If we knew all our good points and if we used them we probably wouldn't have time to be self-centred or to behave in a selfish way. There are only 24 hours in the day! And in every person there is so much goodness. If we used our good qualities our lives would be so much easier for us and for those around us.

For today's thought you will need pen and paper again. Just allow yourself to be very curious about yourself. What do you enjoy doing? What did you enjoy doing before you began to suffer?

Most people who enjoy doing something are good at it. Remember you do not need to be the best at something to be good at it. Everybody is good at something. You are, too. Most people suffering as you do have very high standards. They expect to be the best all the time, without knowing what the best is. Sometimes it is better to settle for what is less than perfect. For today just try to lower your own standards. Be kind to yourself and watch what is going to happen.

'Be content with your lot; one cannot be first in everything.' Aesop

DAY 3   *Feel important*

Do you feel you have to do everything perfect all the time? Today you can try one of the hardest things for sufferers from eating distress.

Most sufferers tend to put themselves under a lot of pressure. You may find that you are always trying to make everything perfect, to make sure that everyone is okay. You must remember that you can't solve other people's problems. You can only help them to help themselves. The same goes for you. You are the only one who can solve your problems. Other people can just help you.

Most people live their lives waiting for the day when the nightmare of eating distress is gone, the day when they can wake up and feel happy, the day when something will come to them that will change their lives, the magic phone call that will make everything better. You need to remind yourself that only you and your attitudes can make the big change and that you do have the power to achieve it.

Today, allow yourself to ignore at least one phone call. You know that any important caller will ring again. For once make yourself more important than anything else. You can leave on the answering machine if you want, but when the phone rings, remind yourself, 'I am more important than this phone call. I am more important than this phone call ...' and watch what is going to happen. When the phone stops ringing, allow yourself another few moments – not to wonder who was calling, but to repeat, 'I am more important than that phone call ...' Does it feel nice to be more important than anything else? If you feel important, can you think about overeating or starvation?

'He who hesitates is last.' Mae West

DAY 4 *A day for the sea*

Mark today as a sea day. Sea, sea air, sea water and the sounds of waves – all this can contribute to a growing sense of calmness. Learning to experience calm moments is a very important part of recovery from eating disorders, and for people going through this condition it is not an easy task. The sea has a special effect on us all. It relaxes us, it gives us strength, it soothes us. If you are blessed enough to live near the sea, promise yourself a walk – even five minutes can make a difference. Allow yourself to see as much detail as you can, the sounds, the smells, the wind, the waves. I am sure you will find a lot of interesting things which you did not notice before. When we are going through an eating disorder we miss a lot of things which nature has to offer to us. The more things we learn to notice the quicker the eating disorder will be conquered.

If you are not near the sea, sit and visualise yourself walking on a beach or around a harbour, or sitting on a cliff watching the waves lapping on to the sea shore. Visualising can transport you there. The subconscious mind does not make a difference between reality and the imagination, so use this fact to your advantage. If it is possible, bring more and more detail to your imagination. The more you visualise, the stronger the feeling of calmness will be.

If you have a video about the sea or sea-world, watch it today. If you have a tape with sea sounds, listen to it today. If not, go to the shop and treat yourself to one. Listening to the waves will help you to visualise. Tapes are much cheaper that bingeing, and remind yourself – you deserve it.

'Take a rest. A field that has rested gives a beautiful crop.' Ovid

DAY 5   *A circle of excellence*

When you are getting up today, imagine a circle on the floor in front of you. Maybe even colour it in your favourite colour. Then ask yourself, 'How would it be if I felt absolutely brilliant?' Pretend that everything is going to work out today in your favour. You might find it helps to close your eyes as you do this and to take a deep breath.

Connect this feeling with the circle and, as you step into it, imagine a special liquid in the same colour as the circle filling up your body, carrying this wonderful feeling of excellence through from the tips of the toes to the top of the head. Each time you inhale, this feeling gets stronger and stronger until you feel that you can handle anything that may happen to you today. During the day, just picture yourself in this circle and you notice that with a couple of deep breaths you will be able to feel this 'excellence' anywhere – in work, school or before an important meeting or interview. Give your imagination freedom. It will work for you.

You can select any state for your circles: calmness, excellence, love, success, concentration .... You can carry your circle with you where ever you go.

'God gave us memories so that we might have roses in December.'
James M. Barrie

DAY 6   *Change the routine*

Are you a slave of your routine? Is your routine connected with your worries? If you break your routine, you can break your worry habits as well.

Start slowly. Try, for example, to have something different for breakfast, switch on a different type of music than you would usually listen to, or change to another radio station or TV channel. Say 'Hello' to people you do not know and watch the change in their facial expression. Take a different route to school or to work, just for the sake of changing and being curious. Do something you did not plan to do at all and be aware of how you feel.

Allowing yourself to break your routine is a first step to change, a first step to freedom. If you are open to change you do not feel controlled by your own rules. You can create and control the rules instead of letting the rules control you. In changing routine you experience freedom, freedom with yourself.

You can fly, but that cocoon has got to go.

DAY 7   *Start all over again*

Did you eat more than you allow yourself, or not enough? Did you get rid of food, or take a laxative? Did you feel that you have to exercise after you eat every apple? Are you fed up of your eating disorder? Don't feel guilty about these things. Let me remind you that you are going through recovery and that these feelings are very common. At least you are not living in denial. You are facing reality – acknowledging the feelings. Sometimes we need to be sick of the sickness to get better.

Today is another day. Yesterday is gone and never comes back, and you could not change this fact even if you were the most powerful person in this world. If you worry about not handling yesterday the way you wished, you may destroy today as well.

Today, keep reminding yourself that this is another day, another chance to enjoy life more. The golden rule of recovery is: Never give up. Never look back. We can waste all our energy on past times and not be able to notice the present. When you have a day that you feel unhappy about you have to learn not to bring it forward to the next day. The past is for learning from, the future is for looking forward to, and the present is for living. You will succeed in the end.

'Success is getting up one more time than you fall down.'
Julie Bowden

DAY 8   *Give your conscious mind a rest*

Do you check every couple of minutes to see if your heart is beating? Do you check every couple of minutes to see if you are breathing? No? Nobody does and yet our heart is beating. We are breathing even without constant checking. Most organs in our body are run by the subconscious mind. We need to learn to trust our subconscious mind.

When we have an eating disorder we try consciously to control what we are eating, what we are doing. We do not listen to the subconscious mind at all. The subconscious and conscious parts of our mind are not in rapport. And if two parts are not in rapport it is very hard to establish communication between them. In recovery we learn to establish this rapport. We need to learn more about how our subconscious mind works so that we can use this knowledge positively.

So, for today, give your conscious mind a holiday. Allow the subconscious to run your day. You might be surprised how easy it can be and how much more relaxed you feel. For example, why not sit down and learn to notice the things around you; take note of how you feel about them – try to feel the moment you are actually in rather than plan ahead to the next moment. Don't analyse. Feel the temperature of your body. Listen to the sounds around you. Focus on the now. Relax and let it happen ...

'We all start out perfect. You begin to see that people become twisted when their natural emotions are suppressed.' *Elizabeth Kubler Ross*

DAY 9   *Does my body want it?*

Are you afraid that you do not know what normal eating is any more? Most people with an eating disorder eat because logically they know they must for health reasons, or because certain foods have low calories, or for some other reasons.

But people who have a strong connection between body and mind know, the moment they look at food, if the body wants it or not. The good news is that you can learn this too.

Next time before you decide what to eat, switch off the self-talk, and just concentrate on your feelings in your stomach. How would your tummy feel if you had this scone inside? How would it feel with two scones, three scones? Is there a difference? Yes, there is. Now you can see that your tummy knows what the body wants. It is the mind that is the barrier. Your mind was for so long pre-programmed with negative messages like, 'I can't eat this. This has too many calories. This is fattening ...' that you believe it.

Good relationships are built up by listening to each other, so a good relationship with our body is built up by listening to what the body wants. One thing is for sure, the body does not want to be overweight, so we must ask, 'Does my body want it?' and trust the messages we get.

For today give yourself a couple of seconds to feel the food inside before you eat. But remember, switch off the chatter box. Trust your body and learn to look after it. It will not let you down.

'If you live in harmony with nature you never will be poor. If you live by the opinion of others you never will be rich.' Seneca

DAY 10 *Accept yourself*

Do you ever hate your body or the person you are? Did you ever ask yourself what hating will change? How often do you give yourself a choice 'to hate or to accept'? Which is harder to do? Which one brings the result you want? Self-hatred is the factor which is responsible for keeping us down, and when we feel like that we eat our shame or starve our feelings. We need to accept that our negative thoughts and feelings have lives and reasons of their own and that it is our responsibility to take them in hand and learn from them.

We need firstly to accept that we did not get our food problem in one day, that it will take time to deal with it and that unfortunately there are no short-cuts or crash therapies. We deserve to be patient with ourselves and give ourselves time.

Acceptance does not mean giving up. Self-acceptance does not mean we need to like what we see. But by accepting what we are, we create more resourceful ways of changing. People who accept themselves are both compassionate and realistic. They are not over-critical. They look at themselves as they are and then strive for a better understanding of what they want to change. We cannot remove a problem until we accept we have one. Acceptance helps us to move on instead of postponing and wanting the impossible.

For today, make conscious efforts at self-acceptance. In the past we have used our weight as a reason for not doing many things. If we accept ourselves as we are, we have choice. Through awareness and acceptance we learn to respect our own needs, values and thoughts.

'The curious paradox is that when I accept myself just as I am, then I can change.' Carl Rogers

DAY 11 *An appointment with yourself*

How often do you feel special? Do you give yourself enough time and enough attention? Most people who have a food problem feel quite lonely and they carry the loneliness with them everywhere they go. One of the reasons why they feel this way is because they do not pay enough attention to themselves.

Now is the time to change that. Make an appointment with yourself. Does this sound strange? Select a specific time of the day, even if it is just ten to fifteen minutes. Go for coffee and during this time deal with your worries and problems. Each time something comes to your mind, either write it down or remind yourself that this is an issue with which you will deal at this specific time.

The more seriously you will treat this personal appointment, the more efficiently you will deal with your difficulties. Give yourself a couple of days to practise this system and you will see the difference.

> *It is the choices you make today*
> *that create the programmes of your future.*

DAY 12   *Every day can be a holiday!*

Would you like to go on a holiday? Does it seem like ages since you last went? Did you ever ask yourself what would happen if you pretended that every day is a holiday? Use this affirmation: 'Every day is a holiday for me.'

When you get up in the morning, step into your circle of holiday feelings. Remember some of the great times you used to have on other holidays, before. By thinking about some nice moments we can bring a holiday mood into our everyday lives and our worries will slowly fade away. If we take each day as a kind of holiday, it will be much easier to get through the day.

The secret of happiness is to learn to live within limitations.

DAY 13   *Laugh*

When did you last have a good laugh? Do you know that 100-200 laughs a day is the equivalent to about 10 minutes jogging? Medical research has found that a burst of laughter can cause the release of endorphins and enkephalins which are described as the body's natural pain-suppressing agents. The act of laughing serves to get more oxygen into the lungs, deepening breathing, which in turn makes the circulation more effective and less sluggish.

Laughing creates internal warmth. It can improve the body's hormonal balance. It is impossible to laugh and feel fear at the same time, as the one activity automatically drives out the other. Smiles and laughter are the best icebreakers at social gatherings. Smiling actually makes people look more attractive, vital and youthful. In order to be happy, you first have to try to look happy.

So, what do you think? You can laugh at this or ...

A smile costs less than electricity and gives more light.

DAY 14   *Push onwards to recovery*

Today, when you have a quiet moment, recapture what recovery actually means for you personally. Write down all the important aspects which you would like to work on and pay very special attention to how far you have got already. It is very important to recapture our successes. That gives us strength to continue.

How will your life change when you are fully recovered? Perhaps there are many things that you would love to do now, but you are waiting until you lose weight or put on some weight, or until you will feel better about yourself ...? Write down a list of things you would love to do now, but are postponing because of these or other reasons. Then look at your list and ask yourself, 'What would happen if I did these things now?'

Doing things now, which we want to do when we are recovered, can bring our recovery nearer. Act like you are recovered and you will be recovered.

Unless we know what we want,
we stand a poor chance of getting it.

DAY 15   *Look in the mirror*

When we suffer from an eating disorder, we usually see all the negatives and all the imperfections in us. That is not because we do not have good qualities, but because we get more satisfaction from self-pity than from self-compliments, from self-credit or from reality.

Look at yourself in the mirror today, just for a moment. Be curious. Remind yourself of at least one good thing about yourself. From now on each time you look try to find something else, even if it is only something small, like your nails, or your eyebrows or your lips ... but without criticism. It might sound very difficult but the more you do it, the easier it will become.

Remember we see what we want to see. If we want to find something good, then we will find something good. We do not force anybody else to like it. We do not try to impress anybody else. It is only for us.

Nice does not need to be perfect. It is the small imperfections that make us beautiful.

> 'The perfectionist is a man whom it is impossible to please because he is never pleased with himself.' Goethe

DAY 16 *Be a survivor*

Are you a victim or a survivor? Was your past not easy? Do you often remember how life was not good to you?

Everybody in this world goes through difficult times. When we go through difficulties, it is not easy to realise that we can use every experience positively. We can be victims of circumstances or survivors. If we feel like victims we have feelings of guilt, self-pity, fear. If we feel like survivors we have feelings of strength. As victims we ask, 'Why me?' As survivors we ask, 'How can I use this experience? How can I learn from it?'

The choice is ours. We are either victims of an eating disorder and then the symptoms take over, or we are survivors of an eating disorder and then we know it will end one day and we will be free. Today, affirm to yourself many times, 'I am a survivor. I am a survivor.'

Move forward in hope of what can be accomplished, and do not be held back by what cannot be done.

DAY 17   *My body is my friend*

For most people with an eating disorder, to be thin is the main aim of life and they pay a very high price for it. How often do you ask, 'Is there any other way of living? Is this thin body worth it? Do you want to be thin or healthy?'

People with an eating disorder are never thin enough. The 'Just another pound ...' syndrome is a part of life. 'If only I could lose another pound, life would be much better, I would be more confident, happier .... and then I would start to recover ...' This attitude is the biggest barrier to recovery. You need to start to recover today, right now and then you will reach the right weight.

Hunger for being thin is the centre of a sufferer's life and this hunger pushes away all other choices. Allowing yourself to think about other possibilities can change this. We can start to learn body awareness just by observing or watching how our body actually works, and learning to treat this instrument like a best friend. It is the only body we will ever have, so we might as well make the best of it. Is it not time we fell in love with the body we've been sleeping with all our lives?

Today, take time out to think of your body as a best friend.

We can use food to defend ourselves, to keep people away.

DAY 18 *What a beautiful world!*

We are all part of a great universe. How often do you feel this? Do you notice small, beautiful things around you? It is much easier to recover when we are surrounded by beauty. There is so much beauty everywhere, but do we see it? Every season nature throws up miraculous beauty: flowers, trees, birdsong, green grass, snow, the unending turbulence of sea and cloud. Do we rejoice in all this beauty? Awareness of beauty is a part of recovery.

Today, take your diary and write down all the wonderful things you can see: flowers, plants, trees, people smiling ... anything that comes to your eyes or your imagination, and remind yourself that all this is for you, for everybody else as well, but it is for you, too.

> '*Don't hurry, don't worry. You are only here for a short visit. So be sure to stop and smell the flowers.*' *Walter C. Hagen*

DAY 19   *Slow down!*

How often is your mind racing so fast that you are hardly aware of what you are thinking about? This happens when we start to analyse too much and ask questions like, 'Why do I have an eating disorder? Why me? Why did this happen to me?' If we think negatively about ourselves, especially our appearance, we can often spark off a whole negative flow, which can continue for the rest of the afternoon or even for several days.

Sometimes it is nearly impossible for us to be aware of this way of thinking. We are so good at negativity that we do it unconsciously, so change is not so easy. Thinking this way can be very stressful. It affects us physically and sooner or later we get lower-back pains, headaches, shoulder pains ... Like it or not, body and mind are strongly connected. If we want to relax the body we must learn to relax the mind, and if we want to relax the mind we can do it by relaxing the body.

The simplest way to relax is to breathe slowly and deeply. Today, take time out for long, slow, deep breaths. It is impossible to feel stressed when you are breathing deeply and slowly. Start to talk out loud to yourself for a while, anything that comes to your mind. Talk very slowly. Listen to yourself. Slow down your thoughts and observe what happens. You might be surprised at how easy it can be to relax the body and then to relax the mind. Remember, the more you practise, the better. It is so easy for us to think negatively, because we have a lot of practice! Now is the time to use this knowledge the other way. Practise positive thinking, breathing deeply and talking slowly.

'In English, to inhale is to inspire, to take in the spirit.
To exhale, or expire, means to release the spirit. All of life can be
observed as a taking in and a giving out of movement and rest,
of controlling and letting go.' Sara Ryan

DAY 20 *Lavender Teddy*

Did you get a teddy for Christmas? If not, go and buy one. Teddies can be very therapeutic and useful. Some people who are reading these lines may think I've lost it, but please continue reading! Very often a teddy can remind you of somebody who cares about you or whom you care about. Just holding it at times when you don't feel the best can give you a warm feeling. It can assure you that you are not on your own.

If you are stressed going to sleep, put a couple of drops of lavender oil or any other aromatherapy oil on the teddy and snuggle up. You'll probably sleep like a baby.

'Reality is something you rise above.' Liza Minnelli

DAY 21   *Step by step*

Do you often feel you cannot do it? Is it harder going through recovery than living with your eating disorder? Do you often feel you would like to give up? Please do not give up. Most people going through this condition are extremely strong, multi-talented people, but because they do not believe in their ability, they do not use it properly.

Recovery is hard work and it takes a lot of effort, but the most important thing is to believe that it can be done. If we are climbing a very high mountain we may not be able to see the top, but the top is there, nevertheless. We can only get to the top by climbing step by step, and the view is usually magnificent, much better than we expected it to be.

Today, visualise your recovery as a mountain climb. Take it step by step and find out for yourself that you too can do it. Assure yourself that the summit of the mountain is not far away. Draw an image of your visualisation.

Life is like a book. The further you get into it,
the more it begins to make sense.

DAY 22 *My body is my temple*

Do you treat your body like a temple? No, you don't? Maybe it's time to start now. One of the symptoms of eating distress is the constant effort to control the body. All our energy is wasted by trying to change our bodies, very often with self-destructive, cruel ways.

If we put all the energy of hating our body into learning to treat it with respect, then our body will change the way we want it to. We must learn to love and respect our body. It is easier to like something if we see all the good it is giving to us. Our body carries us around, give us nice sensations. It is part of us.

Today, repeat the simple affirmation, 'My body is my temple.' Think of the meaning of that phrase. You may be not able to love your body yet, but at least learn to respect it.

'The enlightened man eats when he is hungry and sleeps when he is tired.' Zen saying

DAY 23   *Nature in the sitting room*

Stress is the biggest problem for people suffering from eating problems. One of the hardest things to learn is to relax. We find it hard to be relaxed with people and even harder to be relaxed with ourselves.

One of the best ways to learn to relax is to be surrounded by nature. It is not always possible to be close to nature, so why not use modern technology to help us? There are so many videos on the market dealing with animals, plants, the sea world. What about investing in one of them? Then sit very comfortably in your sofa, lift up your feet and watch the dolphins or sharks swim around you.

Sometimes it might take a while before you can fully concentrate, but do not give up. Learn to develop a sense of wonder and fascination and do not forget that you also are part of the beautiful world of nature.

'Change provides the opportunity for innovation. It gives you the chance to demonstrate your creativity.' Felice Jones

DAY 24   *Learn from the children*

You may have some time to spare today and not know what to do with it. This is the time when we automatically turn to bingeing, overeating, worrying about food, being afraid to nurture our bodies. So what can we do today about that?

Nearly every park has some playground. Nearly every shopping centre has a children's corner. We can learn a lot from children. We were all small once, but all the years of others telling us what to do and what is best for us, without asking if we wanted to do it, had an effect on the way we feel about ourselves today.

Children are much more confident than many adults. Children have an argument and in a couple of seconds they are friends again. Children do not go around reminding themselves that they are no good. Most children have the ability to eat what is good for them and only as much as their body needs. Today, allow yourself to go back to the child's world. At lunchtime go to where you can watch children and imagine you are one of them. Watch how they move, how free they are with each other, how they touch each other, how curious they are, how they use their imagination. Listen to their soft voices, their laughter. And ask yourself how can you learn from them. Allow yourself to model yourself on their sense of freedom and happiness. Very often children can show us what we are missing as adults. They can show us how to be complete human beings.

Absorbing children's natural ability of communication is not childish, it is a way to freedom.

Youth would be an ideal state if it came a little later in life.

DAY 25   *An aeroplane full of worries*

How often do you worry about something? Is it a nice feeling when you worry? Does your worry ever solve any problems? Does your worry about money ever pay any bills? Does your worry about what people think about you make anybody like you more?

People with eating problems worry compulsively. Even if they have nothing to worry about, they worry about that. Worrying is nearly a subconscious way of thinking for a person with an eating disorder. Worry gives us something to do but it does not get us anywhere. Worry takes a lot of energy from us. If we learn not to worry, we will have more energy to care – care about ourselves and other people.

Today, practise an exercise for eliminating worry from your mind. All you need is something to worry about, closed eyes, a comfortable position, and a willingness to use your imagination. Concentrate for a couple of seconds on your worries. Name them and clarify them. Then imagine you are sitting at the airport in the cargo department. You see a lot of different parcels around. Visualise yourself walking around these big parcels and writing the names of your worries on them. Imagine that all your worries are wrapped in these parcels, that they cannot affect you anymore. Now you see a plane coming and taking all your worries safely away. You can even wave them goodbye. If you repeat this visualisation several times, you will discover that you have the power to be a worry-free person.

Worry is similar to stirring up dirty water. You only keep the water dirty. Stirring it up doesn't make the water clean.

DAY 26   *Clock relaxation*

We always think that to relax or to feel better we need to do something big, but if we look around we have everything we need close at hand. We just need to look out from the window of self-centredness, and use our ability to be aware.

Do you feel tense? Do you feel you heart beating fast? Look at the clock. Focus your attention on the hands of the clock. Follow the movements with your eyes. Allow your attention to become absorbed in this movement. Imagine how the gears in the clock are meshing and turning. Imagine how the electric current might be flowing, just as energy is flowing in your own body.

Be aware of your breathing. The movements of the clock can remind you of the ticking of your heart. While you are focusing on watching the hands and the numbers, tell yourself that with every tick you are getting more and more relaxed, calmer ... calmer ... and calmer ...

No wealth is like the quiet mind.

DAY 27 *Place the worry in to the light*

Do you like candles? Who doesn't? There are so many beautiful ones on the market, all different colours and different shapes. How often do you use them and how do you use them?

When we have an eating problem we live hand in hand with our worries. We starve our worries, we eat our worries, we purge our worries. They are our friends and our enemy. The more we worry the worse the physical symptoms of an eating disorder become.

Today, use a candle to practise letting go of your worries. First find a comfortable position to sit in, then light a candle and put it in front of you. Look at the flame, at the light. Concentrate on your thinking and each time any worry or any problem comes to your mind, place it into the flame, place it into the light. You will notice that in a short time you will feel much freer. Our problems and our worries are just extra baggage which makes us feel heavier.

'Nothing lasts for ever, not even your trouble.' Arnold Glasow

DAY 28   *A negativity-free day*

Do you prefer to see bad news or good news on television or in the papers? Bad news is usually more available and interesting, and good news stories are usually a rarity. Did you know that people with eating disorders are extremely sensitive people and they absorb negativity around them on a subconscious level?

To abstain from negativity can actually help our recovery. Why not start today? If you buy a newspaper today look only for good news. Do not read anything negative. You cannot change it anyway. If you listen to the radio and negative news comes on, switch to another station. Music can be more relaxing. If somebody starts to tell you some bad news, ask them to tell you some good news instead.

If you practise this exercise you will see that there are lots of good things happening. We need only to look for them.

Courage is not freedom from fear.
It is being afraid and still going on.

DAY 29   *The leisurely stroll*

Do you find you sometimes feel bloated after eating? How do you cope with this feeling? What do you do to ease this feeling? If you take laxatives or purge because of the feeling, what made you decide to do that? Next time you feel bloated why don't you try drinking a cup of peppermint or fennel tea (they aid digestion and help relieve bloating).

Another alternative is to go for a stroll after eating. Don't go for a brisk walk. Just relax and enjoy a leisurely stroll. Maybe you could go to a place that is special to you, e.g. the beach or a local park. If you get out of the house and do something you will take your mind off the uncomfortable feeling and will ultimately feel better for not having got rid of the food. There are lots of other options; explore them and find out what suits you.

We might lose the ideal, but find the real.

DAY 30   *A list for the day*

How do you feel when you wake up in the mornings? What is your response to the coming day? This morning when you get up, write a list of how you would like to feel today. Do you want to feel relaxed, eager, confident, content, at ease? Write it all down and then write down what you think you'd have to do to feel that way. It might sound difficult but it's easier than you think. What would you advise someone else to do if they wanted to feel the way you'd like to? Take your own advice.

Remember that only you can make yourself feel good. Others can't do it for you. If you feel down or upset, keep in mind that it's not people or situations that are making you feel this way. It's how you react and respond to them. So today, consult your list and do what you think will help you to feel the way you want to feel. Don't you think it's time you felt good?

What we have to learn to do, we learn by doing.

DAY 31   *The power of positive self-talk*

Everybody with an eating disorder has proved the power of negative self-talk. Why not entertain the idea that positive self-talk might be equally effective? Affirmations are one of the choices for this. Affirmations are a technique you can use to strengthen your thinking about yourself. They are strong, positive statements that, if repeated, enter into your subconscious. You can practise your affirmations in front of a mirror, looking into your own eyes.

Today, start with relaxation affirmations:

~ I am relaxed
~ I release myself of all my anxieties and fly as free as a bird
~ I will nurture myself mentally and physically
~ I can handle any situation that confronts me
~ Each day I become more secure and more confident.

Gradually you will find that your negative thinking will be replaced by a positive sense of yourself. You will begin to feel good about yourself, and that is a major step forward on the road to total recovery.

'Let me listen to me and not to them.' Gertrude Stein

12

HOPE – A CERTAINTY, NOT A QUESTION

Hope is a stepping stone to recovery. Everyone is entitled to hope. In eating disorders hope is very important. It can enable people to begin believing in themselves and their abilities. If you have hope then you can certainly recover. If you have hope that you can overcome this condition, then you can.

This chapter is full of other people's hope. It shows the determination of people like you who believe in a better life. The minute you start to hope is the minute you know you can recover. Just like the people who contributed to this chapter have.

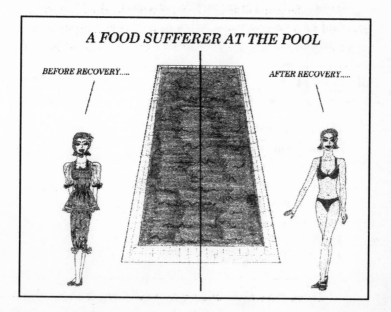

A FOOD SUFFERER AT THE POOL

BEFORE RECOVERY.....

AFTER RECOVERY.....

HOPE

Marie

I went to bed with it,
And that allowed me to look forward to tomorrow.
I built up my life with it,
And waited for it to happen.
It helped me to get over everything,
To do it, to survive, to succeed.
It kept the smile on my lips
And the glow in my heart,
When times were tough.
Something which I could not touch,
But I knew it would never die.
It helped me to see the way,
That the world can be beautiful and wonderful.
It helped me to forget the past and start again.
It was my drug, I could not do without it,
And even now I am still full of it.
It was my hope.

BE POSITIVE

Kirsty

This tunnel that I'm in
At the moment seems never ending
But there is a way out
And if I keep going forward I'll find it.
The road may be long and hard
But it will get easier
The light will appear at the exit
And then I'll walk free!

WHEN I'M FULLY RECOVERED

Sinéad

When I'm fully recovered I will be a much happier, more contented and carefree person. My old self will come back again, that being someone who laughed a lot, played and had fun. Basically I will be the old me again. Food will not be any kind of issue in my life. Instead of being a threat to me, it will just be part of me like it is to every other normal person.

It will be something automatic, what I do to survive, something that will give me energy, keep me healthy and allow me to enjoy my good life again. When I'm recovered my head will be totally free from the stress and frustration I now have with all the 'food business'. There won't be any planning what I'll eat and what I'll not eat. I will never deprive my body of food when I'm feeling hungry. Food will not be like my enemy anymore. I will enjoy it without any feelings of guilt or other kinds of frustrations.

When I'm fully recovered, instead of my mind being fixed on being thin and hungry, it will be filled with other parts of my life, friendships, great social activities and my future career. I want to travel, to be free from problems. I want to achieve a lot from life, to be good at music, my work, have a lot of hobbies, enjoy socialising. Most importantly I want to believe I have friends and that they like me for me, the person I am. I'll have a happy-go-lucky attitude towards life. There will be no negative thoughts about myself. I will be free.

I hope to meet someone special just like anyone else. He will like me and I will allow myself to believe it. I want to believe that this can happen for me. When it comes down to it, when I am fully recovered, the most important person in my life will be me. I will accept all my good qualities so that I can help other people and be a good friend, have good relationships without any expectations, with other human beings. I will be giving myself, believing it is good.

When I am fully recovered I will be real. I will have discovered all the potential that, at the moment, I only dream of having and I will be using that for others and for me. When I am fully recovered I will stop thinking that it is only my thinness that gets me attention. I will learn to believe that there is more to people than their bodies. I will be able to see beauty in others, in myself and in the world. When I am fully recovered I will stop thinking that this is only a dream. I will believe that I actually can wake up and that all this will be for me.

GENTLY LET GO

Sandra

Over the past few days I have learned that life really is what you make of it. Our attitudes have such a major influence on our lives and general well-being, it is unbelievable. Today is the 10th of September 1996 and it has been about three and a half months since I was discharged from hospital where I was being treated for anorexia/bulimia. Even having spent time in hospital being told by psychiatrists and people who love me dearly that appearance doesn't matter and that I am a pretty cool person, I felt no different about myself when I came out than I did before going into hospital. I suppose I could even say I felt worse because I had put on weight. For somebody with anorexia, that seems like the end of the world.

For the past few months I've been getting depressed a lot. Depressed because I'm being kept on a strict eating regime and also because I'm putting on weight. Over the past few days I've realised just how much I've missed out on while I sat here in my room with a calculator and a food chart counting up how many calories I've consumed and how many miles I have to cycle or walk to burn off one-and-a-half times that amount! It sounds crazy and deep down I guess I've always known it.

Something somebody said to me a long time ago has only now begun to sink in and it really hit home. She told me that I shouldn't set out to get rid of all my problems and get rid of all these horrible feelings I have for myself, but that I should gently let go so that I can take them back in a way in which I can handle them. In other words, learn to accept things.

I must learn to accept me for who I am and, taking both my good and bad points, admit that I am okay. Up to now I had a major problem with anybody thinking I was getting better. I guess I was afraid they'd think I didn't need them anymore and leave me, so I clung to my weaknesses, as my friends could hold me up. I was scared of being left to go through this alone.

My attitude has changed so much over the past few days and although it's a short time it has made a huge difference. I have accepted the fact that I am the only one who can break the chains. I am the only one who can change the way I think. I know it could take years before I feel genuinely secure and confident within myself but that's okay. I know I will be fully recovered some day. I used to look to the future and think: 'What's the point?' I couldn't bear the thought of a constant struggle for years to come. The pain was too much. But now, I look forward to the time when I am fully recovered and enjoying every day.

Circumstances haven't changed. I'm still anorexic and I'm still underweight. My parents are still worried sick about me and I still need support, but I know I'm going to get through this. Things will get better. I still have my bad days. Who doesn't? But every bad day is a learning experience and will make me stronger so that I can battle on. My change in attitude has made a huge difference to me. It has brightened my outlook on just about everything and given me the motivation I needed to carry on.

MOVING FORWARD

Sandra

It was 1994 and I was down in Cork with a group of friends when one of them gave me a postcard with this sentence written on it: *Ní bionndúil an sonas gan an donas a bheith in orlaí tríd* (there is no happiness without an inch of sorrow through it). We were in Gougane Barra at the time which, for those of you who don't know, is the place where St Finbar spent his life as a hermit. At the time I envied St Finbar so much. I would have given anything to totally isolate myself from everybody! I was in the depths of depression and I was going nowhere fast!

Now, two years later, as I look back at that time and read the message on the postcard, I can see how dramatically my life has changed and realise just how true that message is. Nobody ever said life was going to be easy. Life is a learning experience and every day is a new day, a new experience. Sometimes we are faced with situations we don't know how to handle. We may go about it all wrong and end up in what seems like a worse situation, but things always work out in the end if you let them. The hurt or pain you may have experienced by doing things wrong will seem worth it because you're not likely to make the same mistake twice!

For me, the past two years have been jam-packed with new situations and many, many mistakes, but I've come through each and every one of them with more knowledge and strength. I'm not saying it's easy – not at all. I felt like I was dragged through hell and back. My life had no meaning or direction and all my time and energy was put into hating myself. It is only now as I look back and see how much better things are, how much better I am, that I realise there is hope. I will get through this. I've a long way to go and I can't do it alone, but I don't have to. The support is there. It's my decision as to whether I take it or not, but it's there. It's my life and I have finally taken control of it. Look at it this way, living with bulimia or anorexia, or both, is hell. The loneliness, isolation, fear and all the tears that are cried. It's a nightmare. Like so many others, I've been through all that. So if every inch of sorrow we suffer counts for some happiness, imagine what our life will be like when we are recovered. We'll be the happiest people alive!

It'll take time but we'll get there. After all, success is the belief in possibilities and recovery is very possible.

LOOK AHEAD

Sinéad

Look ahead
It's time to forget the past
The future is all ahead
There's no point dwelling on the past
Thoughts of wishing you were dead.
The birds fly towards a day
What is the use in wishing
Your whole life away?
It's time to start anew
And stop thinking of what's gone
Other people care too
But it's all said and done.
Parents and friends keep worrying
And blaming themselves for what's wrong
Worrying about what's happening
To the old person they knew, that's long gone.

STEP BY STEP TO RECOVERY

Anon

I have had a problem with my eating for about 9 years but problems with lack of confidence and isolation for as long I can remember. During the past 4 years I have been trying to overcome this. It has been a lot of hard work but I am getting better and it is getting easier. I lived for so long with negativity, fear, self-pity and resentment that it became the norm for me. I'm now trying to change these to positive self-talk, confidence, taking interest in others, self-acceptance and especially tolerance of myself and others. I need to saturate my thoughts with belief and optimism.

It is a process of learning and re-learning healthier ways of dealing with situations. The results are not always constant and sometimes can be subtle. My awareness has improved by trying to acknowledge and concentrate on these improvements. The little changes are important and do count. These are some of the things I am trying and which are helping me:

◊ Reading, sharing my thoughts and feelings with people I can trust. I have been and sometimes still am unsure of my feelings, but this is improving as I spend more time with people. It's important to do things at your own pace.

◊ Affirmations: concentrating on the positive and on the things I can be grateful for.

◊ Keeping a journal of the positive things in any day and the new things I've learned. When I'm feeling down I read back over these things which I may have forgotten.

◊ Visualising and concentrating on the desired positive outcome of situations. Whatever you concentrate on can come true, so I make sure it is something I want.

◊ I find that living in the day is important. I am trying not to think about what is going to happen in the days and weeks ahead or kick myself about what happened in the past. This takes away a lot of the clutter in my thoughts and prevents me from imagining a negative future. I am also less worried about things that may never happen.

◊ Wishing the best for others helps me to get rid of resentment and anger.

◊ I think it is important to believe in recovery but also to have patience. Whenever you hear yourself saying, 'I can't do this' or 'This is too hard', change to 'I know I can do it', 'I am learning how to'. You may have to do this over and over but it does work. It is working for me.

GO FOR YOUR DREAMS

Sandra

Don't be afraid to go for your dreams,
Even if your dreams are your worst fears.
God often leads us off the track just to test our wings
But the strength we gain from the fall and rise
Will lead to better things.

THE FIRST FLIGHT

Anon

I wanted the shadows. I don't anymore.
I ran from the sunlight and hid all my fear.
Today I pulled back the shutters and opened the doors.
I looked outside. I never dreamed it was so high or so big.
The time had come to spread my wings and fly.
It seemed at any moment I would fall.
It's so much safer to stay indoors.
Sometimes where danger lies there is also the greatest of
    pleasures
Pleasures you cannot know if you've never flown at all.
Who knows how high I fly

My wings are still weak and small
My map uncharted
But ... watch me try ...

THE HOPE OF A SMILE!

Leesa

A smile can bring the sunshine
On all your dark shadows of doubt.
When things go wrong and it seems all hope is gone
A smile is the courage to work it out.
When the day's a dark shadow
And forever going down
Keep trying, don't quit
Don't over-shadow your smile with a frown.
When the quitter's given up and declared defeat,
Find the strength from within
Be determined to win
Remember you can't always end up on your feet.
When the days seem like years
And you can't fight back the tears
A smile provides confidence that dissolves all your fears.
When life's a long struggle, and nothing's going right,
Keep your chin up; success is never achieved
By half-trying then giving up the fight.
So when your heart's heavy
Life's too much to bear
Your patience is breaking
And you're out of your mind with despair
Remember your future always seems more worth while
When the hope of tomorrow
Lies in your smile.

'It is not the years in your life but
the life in your years that counts.' Adlai Stevenson

Saturday, 11 May 1985

Dear friend,

I am back to square one again. This month is my birthday. I will be thirty years old. Would you not think I should have more sense? Instead I'm caught in the circle again. So many times I promised to myself I would never do it again, and look at me, sitting here, listening to the rain outside, feeling sorry for myself and really miserable. I suppose it could not be worse. Food, food, bloody food, can I think of nothing else! Why me? Why am I crazy? Yes, I feel crazy and I know I am. God, I am trying so hard. Every morning I get up and say to myself, 'This is the day. I am going on a diet and I will stop getting rid of the food.' Every morning I promise myself: never again. And then in couple of hours I am back to square one.

If I do not eat I feel grand. I start the day with a couple of cups of black coffee, then some natural yoghurts and then for a while everything is okay. I make plans, I allow myself to look forward to something and I am constantly repeating to myself that this is the day and that I cannot go back. I just cannot! And then later, in one flash, all the optimism is gone. I do not even like to admit or tell you what follows.

The evenings are still the worst. The minute I start, I do not know how to stop. It is so hard. I try not to do it in front of Jane. But sometimes I cannot even wait until I put her to bed. Or I put her to bed early so that she does not see me. I am so ashamed, even in front of her. Yes, I do behave like an animal. I know it sounds terrible, but that is the truth. Stuffing my face, fast, with anything that comes to hand. Last week I had nothing at home. And no money to go to the shop. So I opened the fridge and stuffed my face with, you would not believe it, frozen peas. When I eat I do not think. I do not taste. I just swallow. Everything goes in as fast as possible, and then later comes out the same way.

The depression is getting worse. Even the tablets I got from the doctor the last time do not help. I feel like a junkie. I swallow so many tablets a day that I am afraid to count them. Tablets for vitamins, tablets for relaxation, tablets for sleep ... I might as well take cocaine. At least it would be all in one.

But I have to be honest with you, there is sunshine in my life, except I am so blind I do not see it as often as I should - Jane. She is so beautiful. The only time I can stop thinking about food is when I look at her. The only problem is that I feel so guilty that she has such a bad mother. She deserves better, someone who does not shout, someone who smiles more, reads her stories at night, someone who can show her love. But even when I am writing this I am so determined to get better. I know I have to do it, even if it is just for her. I know I will be better some day.

But the question is, where to start again? I think I did not even write to you that I made an appointment with a psychiatrist about two months ago, but it was a disaster. My appointment was for ten o'clock in the morning. I was so nervous I nearly left the waiting-room. When he asked me what was wrong I found it very hard to answer. I could not. I began to talk about other things which were not relevant to the question he asked. I tried to escape the real reason. I got flustered and went red in the face, and the sweat was running off my back. I started to stammer. When he saw me like that he said I have an anxiety disorder and he prescribed me even more tablets. So the day I was expecting my cure to arrive I was not able to tell him even what was wrong with me. At the end of the session he recommended a stay in the psychiatric ward in the hospital. He said it could be beneficial to me.

I freaked out when I heard this. No way! I know I'm mad but I am not ready for that! I felt so furious, a wave of anger flooded over me. I was angry with him and even more angry with myself. My God, can you imagine if anybody found out that I was in a mental hospital! Nobody would ever want to talk to me again. I would be lost, more then I am now. At least now nobody knows. I would have no friends at all, not that I have many now, but I do know a lot of people. Can you imagine my parents coming to visit me! I think not. Mother would die and Father would have another heart attack. I just cannot believe that anyone could suggest I might be a mental patient.

But even whingeing here on the paper makes me more determined to get better one day. Maybe I should start to work on the depression first. Maybe I should just go to the bookshop and start to read what other people are doing when they feel like this. There must be a way out, or at least a path. Yes, decision made! First thing tomorrow I will go to the bookshop or the library and start to read. It is so long since I held a book in my hand. I usually read only diet books or books of recipes, so it is time for a change.

Marie

'Everything that enlarges the sphere of human powers ...
Is valuable.' Ben Jonson

13

WE DID IT

Recovery is more than just getting better. It's more than just leaving the bad times behind. Recovery can become a beautiful chance, a chance to embrace life and be the best you can be. A chance to use your knowledge and past experience in a positive way. This chance might not have been there without these experiences. Remember that you can see the light only if you have known the dark. Without the dark, light would be meaningless.

Read about someone else's beautiful chance in a lifetime and you will discover how to recognise yours.

THE MOST BEAUTIFUL CHANCE

Marie-Aude Louis

Over the span of our life, each one of our hearts is given not one but several chances ... to open, even more graciously and permanently than the most radiant and precious roses. Bulimia was for me, as it can be for everyone, the most beautiful chance of my life. Even during my crises, my tortures, my darkest hours, my greatest isolation, my total incomprehension, I was fighting against myself for myself. My tears had no destination and no source, they were the expression of this inner conflict, this huge contradiction, this eternal imbalance. But I could feel their warmth slowly healing my cheeks and I know this tiny moment of well-being came from inside of me, not from outside. I did not consciously accept it then, but it was like a ray of light caressing me, just as tenderly as the soft hand of a mother.

Still, my mystery lived for nearly five years. Life at the time seemed experimental, my mind attempting so many different escapes, tasting so many different lives and personalities, accommodating so many different environments. And inside of me kept being full of emptiness, though not deep emptiness. Under the layers of pain, plasticity, dependence, fears, coldness, traumas, anger, pride, humanity, I knew the existence of an unknown but true me. I simply and naturally knew, without any convincing effort, that there was a flower lying there, waiting to flourish.

Only when I understood that this self-destructive behaviour would not just fade away one miraculous day, only when I understood this condition was not dependent on my environment, only when I understood that the bulimia which was in me had to be faced, did I really begin the journey of my awareness. And very simply, the more I progressed on this path, the more I felt myself flourishing to the beauty of life. The smallest details of our existence, that we so often take for granted, just like the wonderful action of breathing, became the basics of my recovery, of my rebirth as a natural human being.

The light penetrating slowly but intensely in myself was made of love, the true one which has all powers and certainly the one to destroy the transparent walls I had built in me. Love made itself so present, so boundless, so unique, so beautiful, and so much for me! It did not come suddenly. My bowing to the white throne had not ended, but the importance of the ceremony had substantially decreased. My guilty self-destruction was slowly vanishing, simply by accepting it.

And one day, I surprised myself feeling my own heart entirely full of love. With this awareness of love, I was then able to live and love myself. I finally began to feel my own balance within my own self, between my body, my mind and my spirit. As a result, I developed love for my body as it was, learning to sense its needs of expression, listening to its own words.

As a result, the confusions and the conflicts within my mind, which used to bring physical pain, slowly gave way to clarity and peace, learning to accept and welcome every foolish thought, expanding the boundless world of my imagination and creativity. My spirit saw the light of life, taking its first steps towards an endless growth, opening my heart to myself always a little more with each new second, each new beat, listening to the voices within me, to my guides and angels, embracing my past with all my smiles, cherishing the beauty of my eternal present happiness.

Love, life, God became synonymous. The inner understanding I reached makes me feel every second more intensely, makes me eternally thankful to every person who crossed my destiny for a moment or a lifetime, makes me full of myself and eager to live my dreams.

Not Easy, But Worth It

Anon

For so long I wanted to go for help and to recover. When it actually came to the crunch of picking up the phone and dialling, now that was another story. I lost my nerve and replaced the receiver. Instead I ran to the supermarket and shopped and shopped until there was no room left in my basket and no money either. I went home overflowing with treats. I allowed myself to do that because I knew that once I went for help that would all have to stop. Deep down I was so afraid to recover. One part really wanted it, the other part did not know what to expect and was very scared and frightened. So after many unsuccessful attempts at making appointments the treats followed, and I was more and more out of control. I was so afraid of them being taken away from me and that all that would be left would be the emptiness and loneliness.

How wrong I was. Yes, recovery was one step forward and ten backwards, but my only choice was to live with this monster forever or to make more of my life. I was so tired of fighting, constantly battling, that I decided that it did not matter how much it took. I was going to win this time. My courage often failed, and I often felt there was no point of trying.

But today I see everything differently. My recovery really started when I made it to that first session. Even from there it did not go as easily as I would have wished. But for the first time I felt understood, and because I could not afford to go back, I did go forward.

In recovery I learned that I had an eating disorder. But I *was* not an eating disorder. I was a person. Eating disorder was not my identity. There was more to me. I started to understand more about my behaviour, why I was overeating, starving, drinking heavily. It was just a crutch for me. I needed to learn from scratch about my body, about my emotions, about myself, and find out for myself who I was and who I wanted to be. The hardest was to learn to listen to my body and to learn to respect my body. For so many years I had treated my body as a garbage bin, as something I hated, something I did not want to be part of me. But that is not reality.

It was not a smooth journey. When I was disappointed with myself I still pressed on. I divided the day into minutes and survived each minute.

I had to learn to do things for myself, to find out what I really enjoy. I had to allow myself to feel good and believe that really I am a good person. I had to learn to be more confident in order to beat this condition, to learn too that I do actually have talent, that I am actually a caring person. Today, I am so glad I never gave up, even though I hit rock bottom many times. But now I feel like living, I understand myself much more, because I understand what my eating disorder was all about.

I would like to tell everybody about my recovery, but I cannot yet, because only a few people know about my condition and I do feel that the world is still not enough aware of what it is all about. I hope the day will soon come when everybody with an eating disorder will be understood and will feel free to be open about it. I call myself fully recovered. I finished my therapy a few years ago and none of my physical or emotional symptoms has come back. I now feel free to go for dinner and enjoy not only the people but even the food.

For everybody out there I would just like to say: Recovery is possible, recovery is for you as well. Please do not give up. You can do it!

I WOULD LIKE TO SING IT

Anon

About six years ago my mother noticed that I was losing more and more weight. Of course when she first mentioned it I told her she was worried about nothing, as usual, and asked her to give me a break.

Then other things slowly crept up, but I still did not accept that I had a problem. I did not even realise that my weight was going down so fast. It is hard to describe. I can see it totally differently today compared to how I saw it that time. I was a slave to routine, control, food and negativity, but I still did not have a problem. I thought the problem was the people around me, the people who, as I can see now, loved me and did not give up on me. But at that time I thought my whole family were paranoid. As far as I was concerned there was nothing wrong with me. Oh yes, I did exercise 'a little', but I needed to be fit. I did watch the fat content, but everybody was doing it. I did study too hard, but I felt that I had to. I insisted on eating at certain times only and on my own in the kitchen.

Today I can see everything totally differently and find it hard to understand how I could be so blind.

When my parents and my older sister had enough of my tantrums and my controlling of the household, we had a family meeting. It finished disastrously and I left home that night. I felt the whole world was against me. I walked and walked cross the city, nearly hoping that something bad was going to happen, that I'd finish up in hospital and people would notice that I did exist.

But nothing happened and in the hour of dawn I returned home. My mother was waiting for me. I will never forget her worried face. She was not giving out to me. She was not shouting. She just said: 'You can think that I am the worst mother in the world, but I will do anything to save your life. I will even bring you to hospital. Think twice.' That was different to what I had expected. The thought of that hospital scared me. And knowing my mother I knew that she would. My mum is a very loving, very patient person, but if she decides to do something, nothing will stop her. I did not go to college that day. I was devastated. I felt so trapped. But today I am grateful that she was so firm. I think she saved my life.

For a few days we did not talk. Neither of us would make the first move. Finally Mum asked me if I had thought about the matter and we had a great chat. I still did not see that there was much wrong with me, but I agreed that Mum make an appointment with a counsellor. I went for help. My recovery took a long time. It was very challenging and cancellation of appointments was often on my mind. Sometimes I felt so silly at the sessions, talking about myself. I would have preferred not to be there. At first I went for Mum, just to keep the peace in the family, and to stay away from her hospital, where I definitely did not belong. But slowly I built up a relationship with my counsellor and eventually I looked forward to my therapy. I learned even to speak to her on the phone every couple of days. Life becomes easier when there is someone with whom you can discuss certain things. Not that I could not talk to my mother about it, but I wanted to know what other people do in my situation. Or often I didn't want to tell Mum that I had a bad day because I knew she would become upset, but the counsellor would not.

Looking back I realise how sick I was and how lucky I was to get help. I can only say to you: Recovery is possible. It is extremely tempting to give up. It is a long process of discovery, a test of your strength. You fear what you will discover about yourself, but when you lose this fear you know you are there and the treasure is just in front of you. It is the real you.

THE RIVER OF LIFE

Fiona

What was the crime that I committed that impelled me to stand as judge and jury on myself and to continuously inflict punishment after punishment on my body and my soul? What crime could make me feel so guilty that I reduced myself to feeling undeserving of life, respect or love? Feeling unworthy of love, I set about destroying my confidence and self-image, finding reassurance only in the disappearance of my body tissue. And what was my body tissue? It was me!

I set about becoming smaller and smaller, refusing myself food, and when I did allow myself to eat I increased the guilt of living.

I could no longer think about anything in my life. Food became my life, my obsession, an obsession which I allowed to control me, to control my thoughts and to control my feelings.

Because I did not accept myself or my body, I felt at first that my relationship with food allowed me to control my body, to deny the signals which my body was giving me. At that stage, this was a very exciting power and I could see the results. Other people could see the difference. Their anxiety both distressed and delighted me. Anorexia was merely the initial stage. I began to lose my natural feelings of sexuality and to feel abstracted from myself and from the world. After several months the suppression of the desire to eat led me to bulimia.

I don't think anyone can understand the immense psychological distress of bulimia unless he or she has experienced it. I remember two years before I became bulimic reading an article on this illness. I found the idea unbelievable. I did not believe that people could do this. The idea was alien to me. But what was alien became part of me. It was like being caught in the spin cycle of a washing machine, in a constant state of turmoil which began slowly, but day by day gathered speed until I felt that I had completely lost my mind. I felt so crazy and mixed up, an alien trapped within my own body and with which I could no longer communicate.

In time, little by little, I have begun to relearn the functioning of my body to take back the power which I had given over to my food compulsion. It was not an easy road to follow but at least the future now is bright and new. I know that I do not deserve to live a life full of self-torture and guilt. It is my life and I will decide how I live it. After experiencing the destruction of an eating disorder, I realise how well people can hide their inner turmoil. I've learned that what we need most is compassion for and understanding of our imperfections and those of others. Life is too short to wear tight shoes, or tight jeans. Your waist size is not a measure of your worth or the love you carry around in you.

There is a little well inside us that some call the soul. I like to think it comes from the river of life. This little well is full of pure crystal water, but in an imperfect world it gets muddied. It needs to be replenished and cleaned with love, respect and laughter. My little well became very dry. I felt then there was nothing left. But my soul cried out. It did not want to die. It held me until today. Trickle by trickle, drop by drop, the little well is filling up. A happy soul is writing these lines. I am free. Everybody deserves to be free!

You don't grow being safe, but being willing to change.

Wednesday, 13 September 1989

Dear friend,

It has been a long time since I wrote to you. Have you wondered what happened to me? Yes, a lot has happened. I feel like I have been born again. That sounds funny at my age. But believe me that is exactly how I feel now. It is like another person inside me. Not the two people who for so long were in deep conflict. This time it is the real Marie and she is free for the first time.

Recovery from the eating disorder is like solving a jigsaw puzzle with thousands of different pieces which depend on one another to complete a wonderful, colourful picture of freedom. So believe it or not, I think I have nearly completed this wonderful scene. Some small parts might still be missing, when the old negativity creeps in. But I am able to handle it and cope with it. Looking back, it has not been easy and at times it was very difficult. But on reflection it has all been worth it. All that effort has paid off. My life at the moment is just great. I am enjoying living for the first time. I take life as an adventure, and I appreciate every minute of it more and more. I have let go of nearly all my fears and ghosts. I know I can survive and cope with anything that may come my way now. All those shameful physical symptoms have disappeared.

Yes, there are times when I can feel uneasy around food, but I would not be able to return to my old habits. I would not like to hurt myself anymore. I did it for so long and anyway I deserve more. I have learned to respect myself, and now I see myself totally differently. I am a whole human being, and I also accept myself the way I am, the way I look, and the way I feel. And the funniest thing is that my weight has stabilised. For so long now I have been the same weight. I am not losing any and I did not gain any either. A pity I did not believe it years ago. I could have saved myself a lot of hardships. Thank God it is over. I take it as an experience, a big one.

Do you remember me mentioning about writing classes? Well, I continued with it and started writing a book about all the mess I went through. The theme is hope, because hope was the most important thing that kept me going through that torment. On so many occasions I nearly threw it all in but it was hope that always kept me going. I think in all cases it is the most important word in the whole process of recovery. So you see now I am a writer and I hope again that I will be a good one. It might take a while before I become an author. I do not really mind because I'm enjoying what I am doing. And I know that the day will come when my book will be published. And if it helps one person to realise that there is hope and if it helps even one person to feel less ashamed, or at least one person to get the courage to get better, it will be well worth it. In the end it also helped me to come to terms with my own problem and put an end to all my troubles. Sometimes I wonder why I did not give up, I wonder where I got the strength to persevere. Maybe I was stronger than I realised and just did not see it.

There have been a lot of changes in my life. I will not bore you with the details but just to tell you they have been for the best. The biggest and best of all is that in the future I am going to change my profession. In overcoming my eating disorder I have learned so much about life, about myself and about people, and I feel that I have a lot to share, not only in the book, but in everyday life as well. I feel I have a lot to give. I feel a passion and drive within me. I do not want others to suffer as badly and as needlessly as I did. There is a better way of managing my life than I did in the past. I was just existing, not living. So I am sure you know what I am going to do next. Yes, I've already started. I am back studying and I am going to start counselling. I feel that I can really help people with an eating disorder or who suffer like I did. I think I will be good at it. I want to do it. It is very hard to understand the condition unless you have been there yourself and I hope that I can encourage others to get better. It is a problem that is increasing and there is definitely not enough understanding of it. I feel that the change has to come from people who have been there, from sufferers themselves and their families. Even if the illness is called an eating disorder, it is really not about food and eating so much as it is about people. About their emotions and their feelings and how the illness eats up the person. Food traps can be one of the most isolating and lonely ways of existing. I am not sorry for anything that has happened in the past. Thank God it is in the past. It will stay there and I have learned from it, but I would love to help other people to reach this point too. This is my dream and hopefully it will come true.

Marie

Friday, 24 June 1994

Dear friend,

Today is a wonderful day and I would like to share this with you. So many exciting things happened in the last while that I could write a whole novel about it. I feel like it is only in the past few years that I am living. The person in the past was somebody else, somebody who looked like me but was not me. That was a person who had an eating disorder which made her blind, deaf and dumb. Today it is me, the recovered person, who is seeing so much, hearing the beautiful song of life and feeling all the enthusiasm of life and a lot of love. Yes, I do definitely consider myself recovered and living. All my life I was analysing: Why me? Today I am living and why not? There is still this tiny little voice out of the past trying to tell me to be careful about feeling happy, that something might happen., But today I do not believe that. I take life day by day, minute by minute and make the best out of everything.

I have a long list of all the good things that have happened to me. And as I used to complain endlessly, today I could be listing all the positive achievements endlessly. I even found personal happiness and share my life with a fantastic man. He helped me so much in my recovery. He was always there to listen to me and support me. On paper it looks quite easy to describe how to recover, but going through it in real life is another story. So many times I was afraid that when he found out the 'real' me he would leave me. But he stayed and we survived and today we are happily married.

And there is even more on my list of blessings. I do believe now that I have become a good mother and God was generous to me a second time. I had a beautiful baby girl. And from the time she was born the sunshine never hid for too long. So much for not being able to have children! Is it not wonderful how all the specialists can be wrong. Thank God for it. My elder daughter was my reason for staying alive and my younger daughter showed me I deserve more in life.

I feel like shouting to the whole world: Please do believe me, there is more to life than that crippling food problem. The recovery is worth it. I did it and you can do it too. There is a reason to live and what is more there are people who love you. Even I believe that I am loved and needed in this world.

I have a mission now too. Maybe all these years, all that hardship, was just a preparation, was just another education for my new life. In the middle of the rain it is hard to imagine how the sunshine feels, but knowing that the sunshine will come makes the rain less wet.

Marie

Tuesday, 21 March 1995

Dear friend,

This is the last time I will write to you. I would like to thank you for all the years you have been there for me, especially for all the times when I could not even talk to people, let alone relate to them. I always had you to fall back on. Thanks for the support and freedom you gave me and especially the enormous help of just being there. Now that I have fully recovered and am happy and easy with people I am enjoying relationships again. Yes, I do believe that I can handle relationships now. It is a wonderful feeling to be able to trust and believe in myself again. I have come a long way, and it has not been easy. It has been a long and bumpy road - at times very long and very lonely.

As usual a great deal has happened since the last time I wrote to you, mainly good things, and if they were not so good I took them as a learning process. Sometimes I feel that I have been very lucky but as you know we make our own luck. And at times it is like I get some extra energy for all the work I had to do for all those years. Now I am prepared to make the best of everything that comes my way.

These days I am sitting in my own office. You see, I have taken another step in doing what I wanted to do. Yes, I have a new profession, my dream did come true, and from my past experiences and suffering I have a new aim in life and it has become my living.

I know there is a lot of work to be done in this field and now I am strong enough to help other people survive this monster. Over the years I have collected a vast knowledge on the subject and I am able to help sufferers who are this day struggling with the agony of a food problem. They need support and understanding, and it is a wonderful feeling to be there for them.

Belief in the fact of recovery is essential. The sufferer needs to seek out the right attitude, motivation and support. When people come to me they are so ashamed of their behaviour that often I would just love to go and hug them first, even before they say anything. In the past it was so important for me to know that there is a life after this disease, that there is a light at the end of the tunnel, that there is hope. I firmly believe that I am cured from this condition and if I can survive the agony and pain that I have endured, there is no reason on earth why anyone else cannot do it. If this diary can help someone else to get up and learn how to feel better, then all my suffering was worth it.

You know, my friend, I have been wondering for so long who you are. Now I know. You are Hope. I thank you.

Marie

It takes courage to grow up and turn out to be
the person you really are.

14

FOR THOSE WHO CARE

*When people suffer from an eating disorder they cannot really
see the distress of family, friends and those who care. When
someone is wrapped up in negativity it's hard to think about
how others are affected. The pain of family and friends of a
sufferer is very difficult to handle. Sometimes sufferers push
them away because they find it hard to accept love.*

This chapter is for all those people who care.

HELP FOR PARENTS

Maybe you know someone who suffers from an eating disorder and you are worried. Here are some suggestions as to how you might understand and help the situation. Eating disorders are family disorders. They have an effect an each and every member of the family. Some family members may develop anxiety concerning the sufferer's state of health. Siblings and other members begin to feel neglected as the sufferer becomes the focus of attention. The family's communication and other activities can be disrupted in order to accommodate the ill person's needs. The good news is that although this is often a painful and stressful process, the family system as a whole and especially the communication process really improves if the family, or at least some members, have the desire to change.

◊ Family members must realise that there will be no change without confrontation. It is important that your concerns, fears and observations are addressed in a loving and non-judgemental manner.

◊ Denial is often the first stage of the illness and both sufferer and some family members may experience this. Your confrontation may be met by anger, excuses and attempts to deflect from talking about the real issues. Don't take anger personally. Try to understand that this is a defence against your trying to 'take away' her or his coping mechanism.

◊ Throw your own guilt out the window. Guilt is a negative emotion that can paralyse you and sap energy that you could use more positively.

◊ Do not try to find a rational answer to an irrational problem. You could waste a lot of time trying to find out 'why'. You may need to accept this fact in order to avoid feeling angry and frustrated.

◊ Stop trying to find a single cause or 'cure' for the eating disorder. These are complex, multifactor problems that have emerged over time from many different emotions, experiences, biological and psychological conditions. Each individual has her or his own history to make the disorder unique. This often makes the recovery process slow and complex. You must understand that there are no 'magic pills' or instant cures.

◊ Try to realise that mood swings, personality changes and emotional outbursts are often part of the eating disorder behaviour and of other biological imbalances. People with eating disorder frequently describe feeling guilty afterwards for reacting in this manner, but are often unable to control such behaviour without professional help and nutritional restabilisation.

◊ Accept that you are powerless to make others eat or to stop them bingeing or purging. Often the more you try to control this behaviour the worse it may become. Ask how you may be supportive in helping them to let go of their own situation without taking over. If they do not want your help, avoid conversation about food, weight and appearance. As long as the family concentrates only on the food, the real issues may not be addressed.

◊ There is a great fear and feeling of loss involved in giving up the illness. The eating disorder has often been described as the sufferer's only 'friend', comfort, means of control and means of coping. Unless the sufferer has found positive substitutes for the behaviour, he or she cannot let go.

◊ Do not allow the person with the eating disorder to manipulate and dominate the functioning of the entire family. You must set limits and boundaries to ensure the rights of all members of the household, especially concerning missing food, emotional outbursts, abuse of privileges, stealing, lying and physical violence.

◊ Be sure to pay special and individual attention to your other children and your spouse. Try to separate the behaviour associated with the disorder from the sufferer. You may need to explain that even if you dislike and cannot accept the behaviour, you still love the person. Sufferers can feel that they are bad people and unlovable. They need to be reminded that these disorders are an illness and that you recognise they are worth more than their illness.

◊ Do not try to be the sufferer's therapist. It will not be effective and may seriously damage the relationship between you. No one else can truly fill the role of a loving parent, sibling or spouse. Instead, help your loved one find a professional who understands and has had experience treating people with eating disorders. Realise that the two most important things that you as a family member may contribute are love and support. They are a very important part of recovery.

SURVIVAL TIPS

~ When you talk to your child, listen mostly.

~ Take care of yourself, so that you can take care of others.

~ Always give in to the urge to hug your child.

~ You will never be an 'absolutely perfect parent', so be a 'good enough parent'.

~ Be loving, even when you don't feel loving.

~ Forgive yourself for mistakes you have made.

~ Ask for your child's opinion more often.

~ When there is conflict, focus on the role you play.

~ Have a special time each week for you and your child to do something together. With a teenager, ask for this time; say you need it.

~ Give up comparing your family with others; your family is real and unique.

~ Take time to be apart from your children. It will give you all a chance to grow.

~ Tell your children how proud you are of them.

~ Invite positive people, who feel good about themselves, to visit.

~ You are not responsible for everything going well for everyone all the time.

~ Give your children some privacy.

~ Never criticise in front of others.

~ Think how you would feel in your child's place.

~ When your child gets discouraged, remind her or him of all the things she couldn't do, not so long ago, and now can.

~ The behaviour may be bad, but never the child.

~ If you expect your children to be 'perfect' you will always be disappointed.

~ Teach that failure is never final unless you give up.

~ When your children grow up, they won't remember if the house was perfectly neat and clean. But they will remember whether or not you spent time with them.

~ A positive word or smile every day can propel your child to success.

FAMILY, CARERS, PARTNERS AND FRIENDS

The world of eating disorders can be a lonely and desperate state for sufferers and a nightmare for those around them. Yet there is no quick way of escaping from the condition. Family can play a very important role in the process of recovery from eating disorder. It plays a primary role in how we develop as people and how we see ourselves in relation to other people. Sufferers who have the full and knowledgeable support of their families and friends have a better chance of a full and complete recovery. An eating disorder is not a problem. It is usually a response to some other underlying issues, which need to be addressed. It is a way of communicating inner unhappiness. A person living with a sufferer needs to develop understanding and win the person's trust. Maybe you know someone who suffers with an eating disorder and you are worried. Here are some suggestions as to how you might understand and help resolve the situation.

~ Offer assurance that the sufferer is loved no matter what she or he says or does. Sufferers need to know you still love them.

~ Be there for the sufferer, to listen and give of your time.

~ Develop trust and friendship.

~ Remember sufferers need to know they are valued, whether they eat or not.

~ Make sure sufferers know you are there for them if they need it, but let them take control over their own lives.

~ Learn from what has happened in the past and concentrate on the future.

~ Continue living your own life as much as possible.

~ Look after your own feelings and needs.

~ The happier the sufferer sees you, the less guilty he or she will feel.

~ Avoid confrontation over food.

~ Create an atmosphere where negative feelings and behaviour can be talked about freely.

~ Encourage sufferers to think for themselves. Sufferers go through stages of resistance and denial. You cannot make them overcome this barrier, but you can help explain that recovery is not a 'happening' that occurs overnight. It can be a long-term process and only a sufferer can do it. Learn about eating disorders to increase your understanding.

You are not responsible for everything going well for everyone all the time.

WHAT DID I DO WRONG?

Mother

So many times I lay in bed at night and I asked myself this question. For so many years I felt I was the worst mother in the world. When my daughter was diagnosed as having an eating disorder I did not realise just what was ahead for us. At first I thought it could be worse. She will start to eat and put on weight; she will be cured and everything will be like it used to be, I thought. How naïve I was back them. Ann, my girl, was always a little roundish, not too much, just nice. Everybody loved the way she looked. She was a beautiful child. Not because she was mine, but everybody else said it too. She even won a beauty contest in our parish centre. Then when she was about 15 the weight started to fall off.

At first I thought that there might be something wrong with her tummy. She seemed to be forever in the toilet. I started to ask her what was wrong. But she just snapped at me, and shouted that I was paranoid. She insisted that I leave her in peace and not be following her all the time like she was a little child. Initially I thought maybe it *was* just me being paranoid. Maybe it was nothing at all and I was over-reacting.

A couple of times when I would go downstairs late at night Ann would be in the kitchen making herself sandwiches. I was delighted that she was starting to eat and my mind was more at ease. However, her behaviour was getting worse. I found it very hard to talk to her. She had no time for me at all. Nothing I could say was good enough. It was becoming impossible to live with her. Slowly she was taking over the whole house and we were all afraid to say anything. To make it worse, her weight was dropping more and more. She was looking pale and very sick. I knew something had to be done.

One day when I came home from work Ann was sitting on the sofa, crying. I sat down beside her and asked her to talk to me. She poured out how unhappy and lonely she felt, how she hated herself and told me everything that was happening. I couldn't believe that what I was hearing was real. It was like a nightmare. Not my girl! It couldn't be true. But it was. We decided to go to the doctor. Ann protested but in the end she decided she would go. She knew she needed help. Our family doctor was very sympathetic and recommended we see a specialist in the hospital. We made an appointment and it took three months before they could see us. I cannot begin to describe the living hell that time was for us, but somehow we survived. I reminded myself constantly that as soon as we got to see the specialist in the hospital, things would be different. Little did I know what was waiting for us.

The hospital specialist saw Ann for about twenty minutes. He told her to stop this behaviour, not to be destroying her life and to pull herself together. Nobody spoke to me or advised me what to do. We were back in the dark, even deeper than before. Things were getting worse. I started to read about this illness, but that made me even worse, especially when I discovered that people who suffer from bulimia are usually from dysfunctional families. Naturally, I started to analyse our family. I was angry with myself. I was also getting angry with my husband. The guilt was unbelievable and continued to get worse. I reached a stage where I couldn't sleep at all.

Each time Ann's door was closed I worried whether she was getting sick. I was watching everything she ate. I was really becoming paranoid. In the end I had to go to the doctor myself as I couldn't eat or sleep. I felt so desperate and I wondered if I could cope anymore. I couldn't tell anybody what was going on. I felt so ashamed. I felt I had failed as a mother, failed as a wife and failed as a person. I just had no strength to go on. I started to hate everybody, even Ann. In my mind I was blaming her for ruining my life too. Our doctor was nice, but too busy to talk to me. I was given some antidepressants, which I took even though I am very against tablets. I was simply so delighted to have something to give me the will to go on.

Now, I am not a person who believes in miracles, but I think I may change my mind. One day Ann came to me and showed me an article in the Sunday paper. 'Mum, read it,' she said. It was the story of a girl who had had an eating disorder and was now fully recovered. There was a helpline number! Ann started to cry. We had a good talk and she asked me if I would help her to get out of it. We both felt as guilty as each other and we both felt we finally had to do something. Yes, we found help and Ann is really progressing in her recovery. We had a few family sessions too. We were told what to do and how to cope, living with someone with an eating disorder. I was put in touch with other parents, which I must say helped me a lot. I realised that I wasn't on my own and that there is no need to feel guilty. What happened to Ann was not my fault. Now I am no longer taking antidepressants and I am helping Ann to get through the recovery. It is actually helping me too. I feel I can be a support to her when she needs me. It is a wonderful feeling to be needed.

Today I know we will pull through. I also know it will take time and patience. It has to be done at Ann's pace. But she is trying. Sometimes I still feel confused. What is it all about? But the more I learn about it, and learn to accept the whole situation, the easier it is to cope. It's all getting easier as time goes by. And if the question 'What did I do wrong?' comes to my mind, at least now I know the answer. Absolutely nothing, because I did my best.

I don't know if reading this is going to help anybody else,

but when I was at my worst I felt all on my own. Had I known anyone else who felt the same or understood, it would have been a help. To the parents of food sufferers I would like to say: Please, do not give up on your children if you find out they have an eating disorder. Very often I found I could not understand what Ann was doing and it was frustrating. But it always helped to remind myself that this is not Ann, this is the bulimia. Ann is the lovely person I know, and who will pull through. I believed in her and I still do and her friendship is my reward.

THE GOOD PARENT'S GUIDE

Grace

A simple 20-step guide to peace and harmony in our home:

Letter to my parents
1   I would like my parents to stop being overprotective.
2   Please, do not undermine me.
3   Grant me the authority to make my own decisions or some of them at least.
4   Do not nag me about eating or not eating.
5   I would like my mother to show me physical affection, even if I do not deserve it.
6   Please realise that I know what I am doing.
7   I would like to be complimented, e.g. on a job well done.
8   I do not want to be called names.
9   I want to be able to have a friendly conversation with my mother about small things.
10   I would like my mother to be more open-minded, positive and if possible believe in me.
11   I would like harmony in our home instead of parents shouting and blaming me for everything.
12   I would like some freedom and time to recover.
13   I would like my father to be more involved in household

and family affairs.

14   I wish my decisions to be respected and regarded as valid.

15   I would like my parents to learn to be more tolerant and less judgemental.

16   I would like both my parents to take at least five minutes a day to chat to me.

17   I would like my parents to respect my privacy and not be all the time suspicious that I am doing something behind their backs.

18   I would also like my brother and sister to respect me and not to judge me.

19   I want my family to accept me for who I am, not who you want.

20   I want you to be there for me. I love you and need you, even if I it find hard to show you my love.

COPING WITH A BULIMIC

Anon

B   Don't believe a word I say. I'm a liar.

U   Understand. You must know when to try and when not to try.

L   Love. Don't expect me to. I can't. I yearn for yours but am unable to accept it yet.

I   Impulsive. That's what I am. It's all or nothing.

M   Moods. I have many. You must learn to live with the various forms of my personalities.

I   The person. Myself. Sometimes I would prefer not to exist.

A   Anonymous me, but not forever, I hope ...

A FAMILY AFFAIR

Catherine

I was asked by Emma to write an article, telling my side of the story, living with a daughter with an eating disorder. This is very difficult for me for various reasons. Firstly it is a painful journey back over the past three years, confronting again all the pain, sorrow, anger and frustration I felt during those years.

When I first realised that Emma had an eating disorder, I was absolutely devastated. I suppose I didn't really want to know initially. I had heard about bulimia and anorexia but only in relation to strangers. Nobody I know had any experience of it, so far as I knew. I felt totally isolated. I couldn't talk to anybody about it. I just didn't understand.

Things then began to fall into place. I had been worried about Emma and her eating for quite a while. Her disappearance from the dinner table, her erratic behaviour, her upset and her inability to share her problems were heart-rending. My feelings went from total misery, sadness, helplessness to anger and frustration. At that time I wondered if I was responsible in any way and I was sure that I could 'fix' the problem. I sought help from anywhere I could. I went to meetings, lectures, discussions, parents' groups and read all the books I could find. At the same time I tried to confront Emma. But she wouldn't listen and when I wrote to her, my letter was torn up and put in the bin. I tried to help but was totally shut out. I felt even more isolated, ineffectual as a mother and my self-esteem dropped. This was after a dreadfully low time in my life. My father and both my husband's parents had died in the space of ten months, and I also had a hysterectomy.

After months I succeeded in getting Emma to go for help. I felt a little easier, but things progressed very slowly. The worst day of my life was the day Emma took an overdose of paracetamol. I still cannot think about this without crying. The feelings of sadness are indescribable. When Emma was in hospital, she told us that she hadn't realised how much we loved her. We were heartbroken to think that our loved and cherished daughter could have had these feelings.

Over these two and a half years, I have been out of my mind with worry and fear. The problem took over my life. The pain inflicted on the family was nearly too much to bear. It affected the whole household and it also affected all the relationships within the family. Life centred around Emma, watching what she ate or didn't eat, listening at the bathroom door and trying to talk to her. I had allowed myself to be verbally abused, thinking it would help, afraid to reprimand in case she couldn't take it. I accepted behaviour that would have been unacceptable coming from anyone else. I grew so accustomed to this behaviour and abuse that I didn't actually see it for what it was. I didn't behave normally with Emma. I went overboard trying to be pleasant. I was afraid to challenge her at all. Emma was getting all the attention and I am sure that I must have been neglecting the rest of the family. She must have been sick of it all. The secrecy nearly killed me. Emma would not allow me to discuss this. The stress caused by trying to appear as if nothing was wrong was terrible. I was trying to make everything work normally, but at a huge cost. I was concerned about going out and concerned about going on holidays. I tried hard to say the right thing but it always came out wrong. I was never right.

I worried obsessively about Emma, watching her not eating, making excuses for her bad behaviour to myself and to others. What kept me going was the odd glimpse of the real Emma, realising the pain everyone was feeling in the family. But there were the good days too, when Emma would be able to accept a gesture from me, maybe a letter or a gift, or she would allow me to give her a hug and she would say she was sorry. This year on my birthday, she gave me a very precious gift, a beautiful silver bracelet with a beautiful message engraved on it. I also got a letter telling me how sorry she was and that she knew that I loved her unconditionally. I felt so happy to read this and felt that we could go forward now.

Out of all this I feel that I have become a stronger person. I have learned some valuable lessons. I have coped with difficulties. I have realised that I cannot protect my children from their own suffering. I can only give them my unconditional love. I have realised that I also have needs and that my needs are as important as anyone else's. I have learned that I have absolutely no control over anyone else. I now realise, also, that I am not responsible for this, and neither is Emma. Great credit is due to Emma and all the family for coming through this difficult time and still surviving as a family.

I was very proud that Emma felt confident enough of my strength to ask me to write this piece. I am handing over the responsibility to Emma for her own recovery and I am totally confident that she will come out of this an even stronger person than before. There is nothing, beyond loving unconditionally, that I can do for Emma. It has taken me a long time to realise this. I can only control my own life, not anyone else's. I have also discovered the power of prayer and I have prayed that Emma will realise her own wonderful qualities, which are so evident to me, to the family and to everyone else. Emma has her own tremendous strengths too. I felt so proud that she coped with changing schools, did her Leaving Cert., got herself into college, got her first year exams, first time, and also sat her Maths again and got a great result.

Writing this has been a very painful exercise for me, but I am doing it firstly because Emma asked me, secondly because it might help her, and finally in the hope that it might help anyone else in the same situation. The pain that I have seen Emma go through during this time is indescribable, and I want her to know that my sorrow was for her as well as for me.

Emma didn't ask for this problem either.

RECOVERY IS MY THANK YOU

Mairéad

My life was falling apart.
I felt alone and confused and oh so scared.
This illness possessed me,
But God gave me you.
I can't even begin to describe the depths of my isolation
Alone in a foreign place, but what was worse
Was being alone with these thoughts.
As much as you can never fully understand my torture
I can never fully comprehend what you must have gone
    through.
I can't understand what it must have been like
Watching someone you love die a little each day,
Watching someone you care for kill themselves with
    seemingly little will to survive.
How can I explain what must have been so frustrating to
    watch?
How can I thank you for letting go of the frustration
    enough
To sit and reason with these irrational thoughts.
All I know is that because you did I'm still alive today.
Even when it seemed like the words were ignored,
Or worse still thrown back in your face,

They reached the tiny place in me that had the will to fight.
Little did you know that these words fed this will.
It grew even when I was confused and thought I didn't
    want it to.
To Mum, thank you for all those times you took me out.
    Thank you for enjoying that time together,
    it made me feel worthy.
To Dad, thank you for your unconditional love
    and of course all the taxis!
    You gave me strength when I most needed it.
Thank you, sister, for you humour and realism.
    You grounded me when I had forgotten reality.
Thank you, friend, you know who you are.
    The first person I told
    and the person who made me face this problem.
    Your love will never be forgotten and our special
    friendship will never die.
It's never easy but each of you has helped and with your
    help I'll see it to the end.
When it seemed like my eating disorder had taken
    everything,
I realised it had shown me the love of these
    very special people.
'Thank you' can never be enough, so recovery is
    my thank you
And I owe it to myself and to you all.

The greatest gift you can give to your children is you.

ACKNOWLEDGEMENTS

While my name appears as the author of this book, I humbly acknowledge the massive effort and workload shared with me by others which enabled this book to be produced. I would especially like to thank all the people who contributed their work, and particularly Mairead Mallon and Emma Walsh for the enthusiasm, talent and hard work they put into this book.

A very special thank you to my friends Marie Lohan, Jacqueline Singleton and Maura O'Toole who kept the book alive when I felt like giving up. I would like to acknowledge the inspiration I received from Peggy Claude Pierre and her husband David from the Montreux Centre in Canada; Nick Hunt and Lorna Holcraft for encouragement and support; Prof. PhDr. Svatopluk Jancalek, CSc., and his wife Eva, and Dr Hana Papezova for their inspiration. Special mention and appreciation to Francis and Nicki. Thank you to Dr Kennedy and Dr Flavin for medical advice, and Dr Collins for his training. Thank you to my husband and my children for being patient and so understanding.

And most of all thank you to everybody I have ever worked with for teaching me about this condition and allowing me to be part of their lives.

Marie Campion